LAND OF SINGING WATERS

LAND OF SINGING WATERS

Rivers and Great Floods of Northumbria

David Archer

The Spredden Press
1992

First published in 1992 by
The Spredden Press
Brocksbushes Farm, Stocksfield, Northumbria NE45 7W3

ISBN (Hardback) 1 871739 27 6
(Paperback) 1 871739 28 4

This publication has been
supported by Northern Rock Building Society,
National Rivers Authority and Northumbrian Water Ltd.

Printed and bound by
Smith Settle
Ilkley Road
Otley West Yorkshire

CONTENTS

ILLUSTRATIONS

PLATES

ACKNOWLEDGEMENTS

I am grateful to many individuals and organisations without whose generous help and support this book might never have came to fruition. Amongst my colleagues, past and present, in the water industry, I especially wish to thank Phil Johnson who first introduced me to the art and science of hydrology and commented on early drafts. Many others willingly shared their knowledge and experience, including Tony Clarke, Harry Harrison, Tony Hardwick, Harry Storey, Mike Storey, Eric Watson and Ron Watson. The management of National Rivers Authority have been supportive in the use of records, photographs and computing facilities for word processing and preparation of illustrations.

Expert professional advice was provided on the bridges of Northumbria by Stafford Linsley, and on dams, by Neil Buchanan and Ian Moffatt, who also drew my attention to a number of dam failures.

My thanks are also due to many riverside residents who recalled their experiences and memories of the changing moods of the rivers. Miss Bettine Morant, Clive Hole, Neil Robertson, Eddie Ryle-Hodges, David Sear and A. B. Stait provided early photographs or showed me flood marker stones.

Much time was spent in Public Libraries, County Record Offices and the archives of newspaper publishers of the north-east and I wish to thank the staff of these offices for their time and interest, and for the use of maps, documents and photographs, whose sources are acknowledged below.

I am grateful to Ann Rooke and Brian Allaker for help with map production, to Alan Proudlock for photographic assistance and to Paula Buchan and Dawn Beattie for typing the manuscript.

Generous financial support was provided by Leverhulme Trust for historical research and by Northern Rock Building Society, the National Rivers Authority and Northumbrian Water Ltd. to alleviate the costs of printing and publishing.

Finally to my wife, Bernice, who has walked the hills and rivers of Northumbria with me, I am grateful, not only for her tolerance and support, but also for the very considerable contribution which she and my daughters, Michelle and Nicole, made in extracting and compiling historical information.

Photograph and Document Acknowledgements

Bill Thompson	Plate 1.2
Northern Echo	Plates 2.4, 2.6, 4.2
E. Ryle-Hodges	Plate 2.5
Darlington and Stockton Times	Plate 3.2
Evening Gazette	Plate 4.2
Newcastle Chronicle	Plates 5.6, 6.9, 6.13, 6.14, 6.16, 7.2, 7.4, 8.6, and 9.6
D. Mennear	Plate 6.15
A. B. Stait	Plate 7.1, 7.3
R. Inverarity	Plate 7.5
P. Carling	Plate 9.2
V Blankenbergs Collection	Plate 9.3, 9.4, 9.5
Newcastle City Library	Plate 6.6
Newcastle Society of Antiquaries	Plates 6.3, 6.4, and 6.7
Ovingham Parish Church Council	Plate 6.5
Ordnance Survey	Figs 2.2, 7.2, 8.5 and 9.2

Fig 10.1 is an illustration to 'The Day the Dam Broke' from My Life and Hard Times by James Thurber, reprinted Vintage Thurber Volume II (Hamish Hamilton, 1963). Reprinted by permission of Hamish Hamilton Ltd.

I have been unable to identify the source of a few photographs. I offer my apologies for any sources which have been overlooked.

1. PREFACE AND INTRODUCTION

It is not possible to step in the same river twice.
Heraclitus

More than four decades ago I took my first small steps in the study of rivers, when I first began to swim one-footed in a little sandy-bedded stream in south Armagh. There I learned to stop and divert the flow with a dam of stone and sod, to overturn a rock and watch the scuttling water life, to catch a minnow with a thread and worm, and to observe the rising freshet after the rains. The die was cast: rivers fascinated me then and they still fascinate me today. Since then my river travels have taken me via the Great Whale River on the coast of Hudson Bay, the Zambesi and the Congo to the less spectacular but no less interesting rivers of Northumbria.

The study of rivers has become my professional career as a hydrologist, and the rivers of Northumbria and their floods my special subject for twenty years. Even the annual processing in my office of several million pieces of information on rivers has not dampened my enthusiasm.

This is a book about the geography of rivers, as the creators and creations of the landscape, their interaction with the hills in which they rise, the land through which they flow and the climate that sustains them. It also discusses their history: ancient, as deciphered from rocks, sediments and landforms, and modern as culled from documents, word of mouth and the records of the National Rivers Authority.

Men and rivers have always had a special relationship. The location of early settlement was controlled by the availability of water, for drinking and fish, transport and defence, and later for the powering of mills and industrial uses. The river was not simply a decoration but a *sine qua non*, and a knowledge of the changing moods of the river was essential for the well-being of the community. This book is therefore about people, not the great men who inhabited the castles and grand houses within sight of the river, but the ordinary women and men caught up with the river in their daily lives and sometimes overwhelmed by it.

The main theme of this book is floods, for it is in their floods, in particular, that rivers show their personalities. In a few brief hours, a river in torrent can make more impact on the landscape, on the consciousness of people and on flimsy houses and structures than it has in a decade or a century of quiescence.

The really great floods are remembered long afterwards: like the inundation of Morpeth on the Wansbeck after the thaw of 1963 , or the Border floods of the late 1940s, or more remote in time, the great flood of 1771 on Tyne, Wear and Tees which was almost certainly the biggest in the country in the last thousand years. There is a story of a miscreant brought before the Newcastle

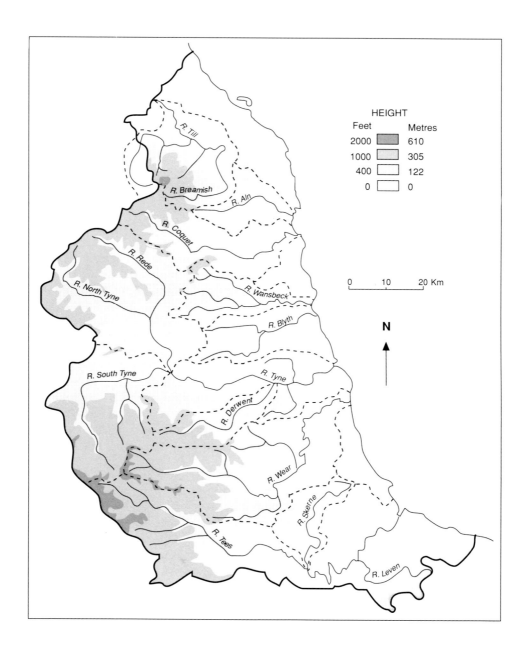

HEIGHT

Feet		Metres
2000		610
1000		305
400		122
0		0

0   10   20 Km

N

R. Till

R. Breamish

R. Aln

R. Coquet

R. Rede

R. North Tyne

R. Wansbeck

R. Blyth

R. South Tyne

R. Tyne

R. Derwent

R. Wear

R. Skerne

R. Tees

R. Leven

Fig 1.1 The rivers, catchments and hills of Northumbria.

magistrates around the beginning of the nineteenth century who gave the following remarkable but truthful responses to the standard questions:

Your name?   Adam
Where do you live?   Paradise
How long have you lived there?   Since before the Flood

Like a biblical personality, he dated his years from a Great Flood. Paradise in this case was an unprepossessing settlement on the Tyne near the confluence with the Derwent, badly affected in 1771.

THE NORTHUMBRIAN REGION

Before turning to some special features which characterise Northumbrian rivers and their floods, it would be wise to describe our region. Northumbria is defined purely pragmatically as the area covered by the Northumbria region of the National Rivers Authority and its predecessor, Northumbrian Water. The region extends from the Scottish border to that part of North Yorkshire which drains to the river Tees, and includes the rivers Tees, Wear, Tyne, Blyth, Wansbeck, Coquet, Aln, and the river Till and its tributaries draining to the river Tweed.

On my office wall, constantly before me, is a topographic map of Northumbria (Fig 1.1), and, as is the way with topographic maps, it is the hills and not the rivers which provide the most striking features. This is a reminder that a river system consists not just of the main channel conveying water to the sea, but also includes the hilltops and fields, which catch the rain as it falls, carrying it over the surface to rocky rills and drains, joining with springs and, through successively larger burns, gills and becks, to the main stream. The hilltops form the divide or watershed between the river systems, and such divides are as important as the river itself in defining the area contributing its water to each river: the catchment.

Ultimately what happens on the catchment controls the river: the water quality and episodic pollution as well as the floods. That is why the National Rivers Authority insists on the concepts of integrated catchment planning and management. Only by understanding the natural processes and the changes wrought by man over the catchment can the river itself be properly understood and managed.

At the heart of the Northumbria region is the River Tyne, drawing its headwater flow from the sphagnum mosses and peat moorlands around Cross Fell, and from the conifer-clad hills of Kielder, where Pennines and Cheviots join. The meeting of the waters from northern and southern branches is at Warden, and it is an impressive sight when the rivers are in spate, first one then the other gaining the ascendancy.

The Tyne becomes tidal at Wylam, well inland, and the estuary of 'coaly Tyne' is much altered, its bed deepened, its sides confined and its course straightened. It is only now recovering from centuries of effluent poured untreated from city sewers, to become once again the glory of Northumbria,

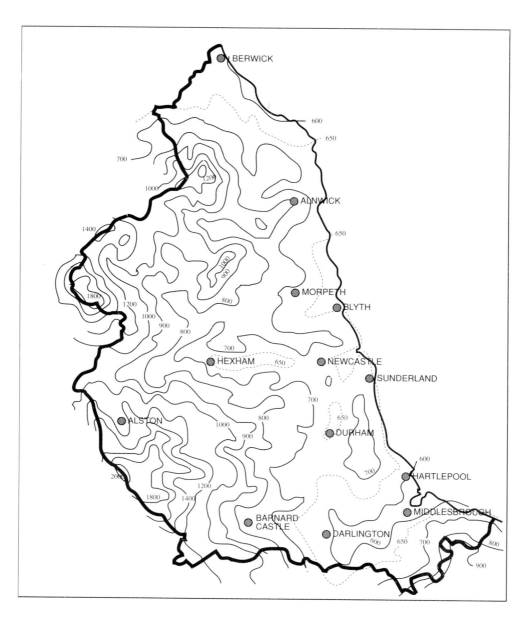

Fig 1.2 Mean annual rainfall (millimetres) over Northumbria for the standard period
1941 to 1970.

where salmon swim and the rising sun is reflected through the spans of Newcastle's majestic bridges.

South of the Tyne, the rivers Wear and Tees also have their sources on the damp Pennine moors. In their upper courses these rivers are quite different in their topography and their fluvial temperament. The Tees drops steeply over spectacular steps where it encounters the hard volcanic rocks of the Whin Sill at Cauldron Snout and High Force or is hemmed in by rocky sandstone walls. The Wear falls more gradually and bears more evidence of glacial deposition in its valley side terraces. The Tees is much the more flashy river of the two: this was particularly true before its upland reservoirs were impounded to hold back part of the flow.

The lower course of the Wear also bears the imprint of glaciation which buried the river's former valley and forced it to cut a new course through hard rock at Durham and through the limestone escarpment to the sea at Sunderland. In its lower reaches, the Tees below Darlington has developed a broadly meandering course with a wide and active floodplain.

The lowlands of south-east Durham and Cleveland receive less than half the rainfall of the upper Pennines (Fig. 1.2). The tributaries of the Wear and Tees draining these areas are more sluggish in their flow but, with much flat land on the adjoining carrs and stells, there have been frequent opportunities for them to spill out to meadows and pastures and into the riverside towns of Darlington (Skerne), Stokesley (Leven) and West Auckland (Gaunless).

North of the Tyne, the rivers Blyth , Wansbeck and Aln are also essentially lowland rivers, rising well to the east of the Pennine divide and draining predominantly agricultural land. The lower courses of these rivers are surprisingly incised (as are those of Coquet and Till), a response to changing sea levels at the end of the glacial era, but upstream from these reaches the valleys broaden out. Along the Wansbeck one such flat area of land, bounded by a broad meander, provided an attractive riverside site for the town of Morpeth. The medieval town centre was built well out of the reach of the river, but during the nineteenth century buildings gradually encroached on the river bank. For this liberty, succeeding generations of inhabitants have had to pay dearly, most especially in March 1963 when nearly five hundred houses were flooded.

The Coquet and the Till mark the northern boundary of our Northumbria region. With the broad upland tracts of the Cheviots at their source, the catchments and rivers are in marked contrast to those of the Tyne and Tees. Being protected from the rainbearing westerlies by the Southern Uplands of Scotland and the Pennines, the Cheviots have a much lower rainfall than the Pennines at the same elevation, and the rain more readily penetrates the grass moorland soils, delaying its progress to the rivers. Thus the Cheviot streams generally convey less water and rise and fall more slowly in flood. Nevertheless, the wide and flat alluvial plains onto which the Cheviot rivers emerge, provide ample opportunity for serious flooding as occurred in successive years in the late 1940s.

TWO SPECIAL FEATURES OF NORTHUMBRIAN RIVERS

Northumbrian rivers and Pennine rivers in particular are remarkable in this country for two characteristics, their flashiness and their snowiness.

Pennine rivers can rise with devastating rapidity: a metre in less than fifteen minutes is not unknown. They may fall nearly as quickly. Unlike the waters of Thames, Severn or Yorkshire Ouse, which may take several days from source to mouth, the flood wave of Pennine rivers is up and gone within a day. The Tyne carries more water at its peak than any of the aforementioned rivers although they drain much larger catchment areas.

The speed of flow in these Pennine rivers can be very rapid and the erosive forces devastating as they tear at the banks and bed and at structures which man has dared to put in their path. A velocity of flow of five metres per second may mean little to the layman but it has caused great concern to the hydrologist attempting to measure it from the shuddering cableway on the Tyne at Bywell, not many kilometres upstream from the tidal limit. It also alarms the bridge engineer concerned with the bridge piers and the scour around their bases.

The history of Northumbrian rivers is punctuated by the collapse of bridges and the gradual development of skills and designs better suited to the forces with which they had to contend. The north-east thus holds a special place in the history of bridge design, in the development of foundations of masonry bridges strong enough to withstand scour and in the design of the suspension bridge whose wider span removed the need to place bridge piers in the current. The earliest suspension bridge in Europe was on the river Tees and by 1835 there were suspension bridges on the Tees, Tyne and Tweed when there were still very few elsewhere in Britain.

Another feature common to the upland rivers of Northumbria is the frequency and severity of floods resulting from melting snow, either on its own or accompanied by heavy rainfall[1,2]. Six or seven of the ten largest floods on the Tyne over the last two hundred and fifty years had a snowmelt component, including the largest of the nineteenth century in 1815 and the twentieth century in 1955. The flood of March 1963 on the Wansbeck was the greatest in Morpeth since at least 1839 and it occurred virtually without rainfall.

Such snowmelt floods appear to occur less frequently in other parts of the British Isles[3]. Indeed, rates of runoff exceed those measured in other snowier areas of the world such as the United States and Russia. Until recently engineers and hydrologists in the south of England have been cautious about accepting the rates of snowmelt measured in Northumbria as correct, since they appeared to exceed what was theoretically possible. It is only in the last few years that energy balance theory has been re-examined at the University of Newcastle upon Tyne and found to support the measured rates of flow[4].

The explanation for this unique characteristic of Northumbrian rivers is complex but there are thought to be three main factors: very deep snowpacks as in 1941, 1947, 1963 and 1979; very rapid rises in temperature and strong winds associated with frontal depressions from the Atlantic; and a plateau topography which allows melt to contribute simultaneously from all parts of the catchment.

Severe snowmelt floods are less common on lowland tributaries with their shallow snow depths, but the River Leven, rising on the North York Moors, is unusual in having a flood regime dominated by summer storms and floods.

CHAPTER ORGANISATION

This book is concerned with the geography and history of Northumbrian rivers, but for most rivers the focus of interest will be place rather than time. The material is therefore arranged geographically, from south to north, with a chapter each for Tees, Skerne, Leven, Wear, Tyne, Blyth and Wansbeck, and Cheviot streams. After an initial river and catchment description, the great floods are described chronologically, but the text is divided into sections on the basis of a feature of the flood or man's response to it – for example, Britain's first flood warning service (Tees), the record of flood stones (Wansbeck), and bridge failure at Hexham (Tyne). Since floods result from rainfall and melting snow which have no respect for catchment boundaries, they occur simultaneously on adjacent catchments and on occasions through the entire region. There is therefore some repetition, especially with respect to the controlling weather conditions.

Two concluding chapters are concerned with more localised but often dramatic events. In 'Flash Floods' the effects of severe thunderstorms on town and countryside are described: peat slides, bridge failure and death by lightning. Finally, more than a dozen cases of failure or near failure of dams are documented both in terms of the effects and the cause of failure.

The text is illustrated throughout with maps and flood photographs. The latter have been collected from a variety of sources and cover the period from the beginning of the twentieth century. Naturally the circumstances under which flood photographs were taken were neither the most agreeable nor the most suitable for photography: driving rain, low cloud and gathering dusk, and sometimes photos were taken by amateur observers with poor equipment. They nevertheless provide a unique glimpse of unrepeatable events and I would like to acknowledge the skill and the persistence of the photographers.

I have balanced the score by including some photographs of the delights of Northumbrian rivers in more cheerful moods.

HISTORICAL SOURCES

The scientific collection of data on river flow and floods commenced in Northumbria only in the 1950s after the River Boards Act of 1948, which required the Boards to install gauging stations. The record of floods before that time has been compiled from a wide variety of sources, of which the following is a summary:

1. For the period immediately prior to gauged records, information was obtained from recent interviews with riverside inhabitants, and from the records of earlier interviews carried out by River Authority staff.

2. Fortunately rainfall records extend much further back in time than those for river flow. Long-term records of daily rainfall and snow were examined from

1861 and all exceptional totals noted as potential dates of floods. Further useful information was provided by the publication, *British Rainfall*[5].

3. Published local records such as those of Richardson (1846)[6], Sykes (1833)[7] and Fordyce (1857)[8], and unpublished compilations (notably those of Duncan)[9], provided a basis for extension much further back in time. These records normally cover the full range of historical phenomena but in 1849 Richardson[10] also compiled a separate record of floods. This was the single most useful early source. A more recent compilation has been made by Jones and colleagues in 1984 for selected areas of the United Kingdom[11].

4. The list of dates from rainfall and local records permitted a more efficient search of regional and local newspapers. Regional newspapers based on Newcastle upon Tyne commenced in 1710 (*Newcastle Gazette*), and, by the mid-nineteenth century, most provincial towns had their own paper. The search was assisted by the practice of referring to previous large floods and by cross checking between rivers.

5. Flood stones and flood marks engraved on riverside buildings and structures provide valuable and precise information for making comparisons of the severity of floods. The practice seems to have started after the flood of 1771 for which five flood marks still exist along the lower Tyne.

6. Early information was obtained primarily from published diaries (e.g. Hodgson 1910[12]), unpublished diaries, parish registers, and reports of County Quarter Sessions. Administrative orders were made at Quarter Sesions concerning the repair of bridges and highways consequent upon flood damage. These latter records date back to the early seventeenth century.

Together these sources give a fairly comprehensive list of floods back to the mid–eighteenth century which in several cases can be ranked in order of severity. Earlier reports tend to produce only a vague idea of flood occurrence with some colourful if imprecise local details.

ENGINEERING IMPLICATIONS OF GREAT FLOODS

The historical study of rivers and their floods has important implications for engineering design in, or adjacent to, rivers. But first a little technical explanation is necessary.

Dams, bridges and culverts are designed to convey floodwater safely. Embankments are designed to protect buildings and property from flooding. With the exception of major dams and protection of nuclear power stations, such structures are not designed to convey, or protect against, the biggest flood that could occur on a given river, but some lesser flood with a specified risk of occurrence. Such risk is usually expressed in terms of a return period, which is the average interval between floods of a given magnitude. Thus a culvert on a minor road may be designed to carry a five-year return period flood; embankments to protect houses for a forty-to-a-hundred-year return period and bridges to withstand a flood of several hundred-year return period. The decision on the level of protection depends both on the cost of the structure and the costs and consequences of its failure.

Another way of expressing such a design flood is in terms of the odds against its occurrence in a given year. Thus a forty-year return period flood has forty to one odds against occurrence in a particular year. Expressing the design flood in this way removes the misconception that if we have just had a forty-year return period flood, we are safe for the next forty years. In the horse racing analogy, forty to one outsiders can win successive races!

Unfortunately the longest scientifically measured record of flow in Northumbria is just over thirty years and in most rivers the record is much shorter. This is insufficient for reliable design of major structures which may require return periods of over a hundred years. There are dangers of designing flood protection structures of insufficient height or strength with consequent structural damage or failure, or of designing them unnecessarily large and costly.

HISTORIC FLOODS AND CLIMATIC CHANGE

The design of river structures has traditionally been based on the assumption of a stable climate. Although the weather changes, and one year differs from another, over a period of time the main statistics of climate are assumed not to change. At least where natural catchments are concerned, the statistics on which flood designs are based are also assumed to remain the same.

Of course this has never been quite true. On a very long time scale, the Ice Age provides a demonstration of a vastly different world climate and there is evidence of another less severe but more recent cold period, the Little Ice Age from about 1500 to 1850. Such changes appear to result primarily from variations in solar activity and from peculiarities in the earth's orbit about the sun[13]. On a shorter time scale, the influence of major natural terrestrial events on global climate can also be seen. Such an event was the explosive eruption of Krakatoa in Indonesia in 1883, which is estimated to have thrown twenty cubic kilometres of ash high into the atmosphere. Fine dust was distributed round the earth by high winds in the lower stratosphere, veiling the sun. Not only did it influence global temperature and rainfall pattern for a time, but it may also have inspired the startling colours of Impressionist sunsets of the late nineteenth century. In 1991 the eruption of Pinatubo in the Philippines threatens to create a similar screen to incoming solar radiation[14].

Now, climatic change of a less natural kind is in the news. Gases are being emitted which enhance the greenhouse effect of the earth's atmosphere. The protective ozone layer in the upper atmosphere is being depleted and there are dire predictions of increasing temperatures, rising sea levels, and changing distributions of world rainfall and severity of storms. There is a popular tendency to link every short term change or weather extreme, local or global, to the greenhouse effect: the English drought of 1989-90, the Scottish floods of February 1990, the floods of Bangladesh and the spreading of the Sahara.

Whilst there may be some linkage between such events and climatic change, it is almost impossible to distinguish the effects of climate change from the natural variability of a stable climate, especially where our detailed knowledge of that climate and the resulting river flows is restricted to a few decades. We need to extend our knowledge back in time to discover the range of possibilities of climate and river flow before the warming trend got under way. We would like to know, for example, whether the recent decades with scientific observations were typical of the last few centuries. Have there been changes, cyclic or otherwise, in severity and frequency of flooding? How do the largest recently observed floods compare with the largest historical events?

Some of these questions have been addressed on a national or continental scale by climatologists and hydrologists. For example, extensive work has been done by the British Meteorological Office and by the Climatic Research Unit of the University of East Anglia, under the leadership of Professor Lamb [15]. There were earlier broad-based studies of historical climate and flooding by Manley (1953)[16] Brooks and Glasspoole (1928)[17]. However, much additional understanding can be gained by the detailed analysis of historical records from individual rivers, especially where the flooding information is comprehensive and quantifiable.

I do not intend to describe statistical analysis of floods which would do little to excite the interest of the general reader. However, I hope to present the material so that it can be used as a source for studies such as, for example, I carried out for the River Wear[18]. I hope that this will not conflict with the objective of providing a readable account of the rivers and their historic floods.

Some preliminary results of these scientific and statistical studies may be of general interest:

1. The largest historical flood on the rivers Tyne, Wear and Tees occurred in November 1771. It is probable that the flow in this extraordinary flood was at least twice the highest measured in recent decades and more than fifty percent higher than the next biggest flood over several centuries. Recent hydraulic analysis on the lower River Tyne based on flood level marks, suggests a flow of around four thousand cubic metres per second, a figure far greater than has previously been recorded or suggested for any British river.[19] In contrast the comparatively recent flood of 1963 on the river Wansbeck was the greatest since at least 1839.
2. Analysis on the river Wear suggests that, since measured records began in 1957, flooding has not been as frequent or severe as over the period as a whole since 1750.
3. Periods of more and less frequent flooding, covering one to several decades, are a feature of the record, and are common to most of the rivers of the region. Thus the periods of most intense flooding were the 1770s and 1870 to 1903. These compare sharply with periods of quiescence at the turn of the nineteenth century (1790-1810) and the beginning of the twentieth century (1903-30).

These results lead to the conclusion that the recent, scientifically measured record of river flows is not fully representative of the longer historic period. It would therefore be unwise to attribute future departures from recent flooding experience solely to the influence of global warming.

Plate 1.1 A mossy headwater spring on the slopes of Cross Fell. *Photo D. Archer*

Plate 2.1 Wearside harbour transformed by twilight. *Photo Bill Thompson*

A MATTER OF TIME

To avoid confusion between dates quoted here and in other publications, a brief explanation of earlier date referencing systems is necessary.[20]

The present Gregorian calendar started in Britain on 13 September 1752 (which followed 2 September in the Julian calendar). The ten lost days were to compensate for a surplus of leap years in the Julian calendar. Some scientific writers, in order to place weather events in their correct seasonal context, quote dates before 1752, adjusted to the Gregorian calendar. In this book the original Julian day and month dates are used.

At the same time, in 1752, the opportunity was taken to fix the start of the year on 1 January, although some sources had adopted this continental practice earlier. From 1153 to 1751, the year had begun on the day of the Annunciation of St Mary, 25 March. Thus 24 March 1705 was followed next day by 25 March 1706. There can sometimes be confusion in determining the year of events between January and March. I have used the Gregorian system to reference years: the January to December year.

MIXED MEASURES

Purists may be unhappy with the mixture of units used in the text, but there are good reasons for the dual system. The conversion of approximate statements of depth in Imperial units to their metric equivalents would give a spurious impression of accuracy and in some cases would remove the poetry of the original expression: 'the Tyne rose a yard perpendicular' is altogether more pleasing than 'the Tyne rose 0.91 metres'. As a purveyor of data to the public I am also aware of a continued preference amongst older generations for inches, feet and gallons. Where historic descriptions are concerned, therefore, the original Imperial units have been preserved.

However, in matters scientific, and for measurements made in the recent past, I have reverted to the simplicity of the metric system. In a few instances, I have quoted both units. The following table provides conversions for units most commonly used.

Length

1 inch = 25.4 millimetres	1 millimetre = 0.039 inches
1 foot = 0.305 metres	1 metre = 3.28 feet
1 yard = 0.91 metres	1 metre = 1.094 yards
1 mile = 1.609 kilometres	1 kilometre = 0.621 miles
1 perch = 5.02 metres	

Area

1 acre = 0.405 hectares	1 hectare = 2.471 acres
1 sq mile = 2.57 sq kilometres	1 sq kilometre = 0.386 sq miles

Velocity

1 foot/sec = 0.305 metres/sec	1 metre/sec = 3.28 feet/sec
= 1.10 km/hour	= 2.24 miles/hr

Volume
1 Imperial Gallon = 4.55 litres   1 litre = 0.22 gallons

Flow
1 million gallons/day (Mgd) = 0.053 cubic metres/sec (cumec)
                                                  1 cumec = 19.0 Mgd

REFERENCES
1. Archer, D. R. 'Severe snowmelt runoff in northeast England and its implications', Proc. Instn Civil Engrs, pt 2, 71 (1981)
2. Archer, D. R. 'Computer modelling of snowmelt flooding in northeast England', Proc. Instn Civil Engrs, pt 2, 75 (1983)
3. Archer, D. R. and Johnson, P. 'The hydrological significance of snow in Britain', Proc. of WMO Symposium, Banff, Canada (1972)
4. Mawdsley, J. A., Dixon, A. K. and Adamson, A. C. 'Extreme snowmelt in the United Kingdom', *Proc of the Third National Symposium, British Hydrological Society*, Southampton (1991)
5. *British Rainfall.* 1860–1968
6. Richardson, M. A. *The Borderer's Table Book or Gathering of the Local History and Romance of the English and Scottish Border.* Historical Division, (5 vols, Newcastle upon Tyne, 1846)
7. Sykes, J. *Local Records or Historical Register of Remarkable Events from the Earliest Period of Authentic Record to the Present Time*, (Newcastle upon Tyne, 1833)
8. Fordyce, T. *Local Records or Historical Register of Remarkable Events which have occurred in Northumberland and Durham*, (Newcastle upon Tyne, 1867 and 1876)
9. Duncan, W. Local newspaper cuttings 1878–1915. Unpublished compilation, 1 vol. per year. Newcastle public library.
10. Richardson, M. A. *Memorials of the Floods in the Rivers of Northumberland and Durham*, (Newcastle upon Tyne, 1849)
11. Jones, P. D., Oglivie, A. E. J. and Wigley, T. M. L. 'Riverflow Data for the United Kingdom: Reconstructed Data back to 1844 and Historical Data back to 1556' *University of East Anglia, Climatic Research Unit Research Report* no 8 (1984)
12. Hodgson, J. C. (ed) *Six North Country Diaries*, Surtees Society, no 118, (Durham, 1910)
13. Gribben, J. *The Climatic Threat*, (London, 1978)
14. Joyce, C. 'Volcano Clouds the Picture in Global Warming', *New Scientist*, 1783, (1991)
15. Lamb, H. H. *Climate: Present Past and Future*, (London, 1977)
16. Manley, G. *Climate and the British Scene*, (London, 1953)
17. Brooks, C. E. P. and Glasspoole, J. *British Floods and Droughts*, (London, 1928)
18. Archer, D. R. 'Improvement in flood estimates using historical flood information on the River Wear at Durham', *Proc. First National Hydrology Symposium, British Hydrological Society*, Hull (1987)
19. Archer, N. 'Estimating the discharge of historical floods on the river Tyne at Hexham', Unpublished M. Eng Project, University of Birmingham, (1991)
20. Potter, H. R. 'The use of historic records for the augmentation of hydrological data', *Institute of Hydrology Report*, 46 (1978)

Plate 2.1 The bright green moss of the flushes contrasts with the bleached winter grasses where the headwaters of the Tees spring below Cross Fell. Upper Tees is in the middle distance, Burnhope Seat on the horizon left, and Cow Green on right. *Photo. D. Archer.*

Plate 2.2 Low Force tumbles over the hard rocks of the Whin Sill at Newbiggin-in-Teesdale. *Photo. D. Archer.*

2. THE RIVER TEES

Contagious fogs which falling on the land,
Have every pelting river made so proud
That they have overborne their continents
Shakespeare A Midsummer Night's Dream
Act 2, Scene 1

The river Tees rises on the south-eastern slopes of Cross Fell, the highest summit of the Pennines (893 metres). From there, I have often looked out to the west and far below to the green and chequered floor of the Eden valley and to the east across a broad expanse of grass and heather moorland stretching to Burnhope Seat (Fig. 2.1). Clear springs emerge from dark green or golden flushes of mosses and liverworts at the base of the Cross Fell screes and tumble steeply over moss-covered rocks (Plate 2.1). On a summer morning it is a scene of unbelievable grandeur.

But the Tees is a river of contrasts and extremes. At the same place on a different occasion, it can be as impressive in its desolation. Cloud rolls in rapidly from the west, obscures the sun and settles over Cross Fell, Great and Little Dun Fell and Knock Fell. There is no easy escape from the cloud, wind and rain, for it is a long way to Dufton or Garrigill, as many a walker of the Pennine Way has discovered. Underfoot the peat can become a quagmire where denuded of vegetation and eroded by rain and tramping feet.

The moors around Cross Fell have the highest and most persistent rainfall in the Pennines, with annual totals of more than 2000 millimetres, and there is little chance for the water to soak into already saturated peat or impermeable rock. Most of the rain reaches the river within minutes. The rivers carry much water and are frequently in spate.

Winter precipitation in the upper reaches of the Tees catchment often falls as snow. On average the snow lies for nearly two months at Moorhouse at 550 metres above sea level, near the confluence of the Tees and Trout beck. In 1979 there was still enough snow for skiing on Midsummer's day. In the grip of winter, the rivers themselves, concealed beneath a cover of drifted snow are deeply frozen, and flow may cease entirely as it did in 1963. When the thaw does arrive, it produces floods of high volume and exceptional duration in the lower reaches of the river.

The Trout beck catchment is of special importance both as the core of the Teesdale National Nature Reserve, and also as a site since 1991 for Britain's contribution to the study of global climatic change. As a catchment little changed by the hand of man and preserved from future man-made change by its status as a nature reserve, it was an ideal site for the TIGER (Terrestrial Initiative in Global Environmental Research) programme. Climate and river

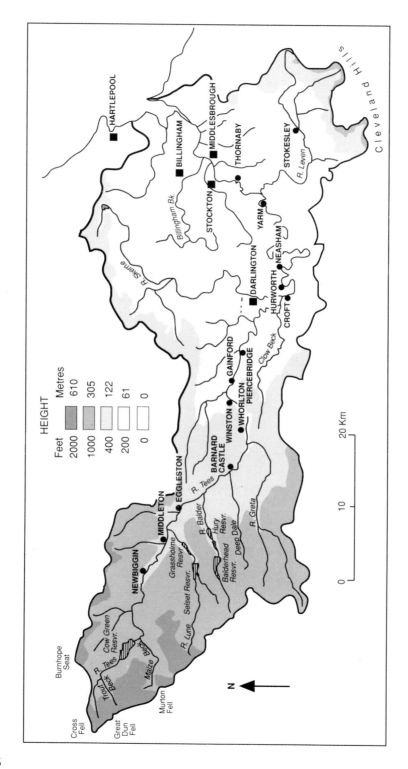

Fig 2.1 The river Tees and its catchment.

flows are carefully monitored to provide the next generation with evidence for climatic change.

A short distance downstream, however, there has been a fundamental change to the river where a massive concrete and earth dam, twenty-one metres high, holds back forty million cubic metres of water in Cow Green Reservoir. The dam was completed in 1970 to provide water to meet the growing industrial thirst of Teesside.

It does so by regulating the flow in the river Tees, storing in times of plenty and releasing sufficient to abstract in the lower reaches in times of low flow. Like the other reservoirs of the upper Tees, Cow Green also exerts a control on high flows in the river and reduces its natural tendency to spill out in its lower reaches.

At Cow Green the power of engineering competes for attention with the majesty of nature for, immediately below the dam, the water gushes from Cauldron Snout, part rapid and part waterfall, dropping forty metres over a length of four hundred metres. Cauldron Snout, like the other great waterfall of the Tees at High Force, owes its existence to the Whin Sill, a band of hard volcanic rock which has resisted erosion. At High Force, the river drops twenty-one metres vertically and, even with some of the headwater flow held back by Cow Green reservoir, it can be a spectacular sight with a flow of more than three hundred cubic metres per second.

There are many other picturesque stretches in its upper and middle reaches where the Tees tumbles over rapids or glides in deep pools enclosed between sheer rock walls, on a rocky or boulder-strewn bed (Plate 2.2). It is the steepness of its channel that makes the Tees extreme in its response to rainfall. The water can rise very quickly especially in summer, by as much as a metre in fifteen minutes, creating the 'Tees wave' or 'Tees roll'. It is highly probable that the 'roll' has caused more mishaps and claimed more lives in moderate floods than inundation in the most extreme ones.

In spite of the potential for high discharges there is little overbank flooding in the upper and middle reaches of the river because the channel is deeply incised, except between Middleton and Eggleston. However, buildings and structures adjacent to the river especially at Barnard Castle have suffered in the greatest floods.

The nature of the river changes as it passes the town of Darlington. The valley opens out and the river follows a meandering course in an alluvial channel on a broad floodplain. As the crow flies it is thirty kilometres from Darlington to the mouth of the Tees but the river travels seventy-five kilometres on the same journey. The slope of the channel becomes gentler; the river falls only thirty metres from Darlington to the sea. In this reach the river spills out once every two or three years on to a limited area of the floodplain. On occasions a very extensive area of lowland within the loops of the meanders has been inundated, affecting farmhouses and property in the riverside villages of Croft, Neasham and Yarm.

Tributaries to this lower reach of the Tees drain a catchment area of several hundred square kilometres, yet they usually add little to the flood flow of the main river, generated in the Pennines. Rainfall in these lowland catchments is much less than on the hills (Fig 1.2). Average annual rainfall is typically around seven hundred millimetres but is as low as five hundred and seventy millimetres at Stockton. In 1989, the lowest annual total ever recorded in Britain of 342 millimetres occurred at Hartburn Grange west of Stockton. In these areas, the agricultural soils have a much greater capacity to absorb rainfall and often less than ten percent of storm rainfall reaches the channel compared with over sixty percent in the Pennines. Nevertheless, because of their limited natural capacity, lowland tributaries such as the river Skerne have themselves caused extensive flooding of agricultural land and housing adjacent to their courses, described in Chapter 3.

The river Leven is a special case for it rises in the uplands of the North York Moors with short steep sections disgorging onto the plain and periodically causing severe flooding in Stokesley and Great Ayton. By the time it joins the main Tees below the tidal limit, it has assumed the character of a lowland river. Leven floods are described in Chapter 4.

The Tees is indeed a river of contrasts and these are reflected in the suggestions as to the origin and meaning of its name. The most widely held view[1] is that 'Tees' is related to the old Celtic word 'tes' meaning heat, presumably (when applied to a river) in the sense of surging and bubbling, a description highly appropriate to the upper reaches. An older interpretation[2] is 'winding' (from Celtic 'taoi'), a term clearly applicable to the meandering channel of the lowlands.

EARLY FLOOD HISTORY
Knowledge of floods in the Tees before 1750 is sketchy as in other Northumbrian rivers. The earliest information is from 1356 when, after a great flood, 'the good men of Croft' were granted an allowance for keeping the bridge in repair[3]. In 1531 water undermined 'the grete bridge at Croft . . . being of six myghtye large pillars and of seven arches of stone workes' and damaged the structure so that a local tax for repairs was levied[4].

During the seventeenth century, information comes from the quarter sessions bridge accounts[5,6], concerned with the repair of bridges after flood damage. Because the Tees formed the county boundary between Durham and the North Riding, the two counties were each charged with the responsibility for maintaining their portion of the bridges. Reference to floods causing damage to Tees bridges at Croft and Yarm may therefore appear in reports of either county.

North Riding accounts refer to two winter floods in the seventeenth century, one in 1624 and the other in 1684 when great damage was done to Yarm bridge. The latter event was almost certainly due to melting snow for Robert Stock comments that in the winter of 1684 there was a terrible frost and much snow from the end of November to mid February[7,8]. An order was made at the Durham quarter sessions in 1638 for the repair of 'Yarum' bridge which is 'broken up and decayed'. This may have been the consequence of a major flood in 1635 noted in the *Gentleman's Magazine*. Several further floods are noted in the diary of Christopher Sanderson of Barnard Castle which covers the period from 1640 to 1688[9,10]. On 20 December 1672 the Tees was 'exceeding great', following a sudden thaw, and damage was done at Barnard Castle and many other places. Flooding is mentioned in January 1674 and again in 1682: 'Monday morning ye 15th January early ye Teese came out and was exceeding great as in the manner it was ever knowne'.

In none of these early events is there any indication of levels reached or property flooded which could be used as a basis for comparison of magnitudes with later events. After 1684 no records of flooding on the Tees have been found until 1753. In view of the growth of printed and published information during the eighteenth century, it must be assumed that no record implies no flooding of any significance: this was a remarkably flood-free period.

THE FLOOD OF 1753

The long absence of floods could have encouraged building adjacent to the river and the growth of riverside villages. It also accounts for the degree of consternation and the extent of damage during the flood of 1753[11]. Indeed Graves[12], in his account of the town of Yarm, dates the beginning of its decline as a port to this flood.

The flood was preceded by a period of heavy snowfall on 14 and 15 February. The thaw set in on the 16th with a strong westerly wind and rain. There are no accounts of the flood in the upper reaches but at Stapleton the boatman said the water was higher by 'a yard and a half in level' than ever known before[13].

At Croft the water came into the turnpike houses at the end of Croft bridge and forced the gatekeeper, William Burleston, to abandon his house and seek refuge for the night at a higher level on the bridge. One wall of his house was broken down and fifty pounds of the toll money was lost in the water. It almost submerged the village of Neasham 'having destroyed every house except one to which all the people resorted and by good luck saved their lives, though with the loss of all their cattle and stacks of hay and corn'[14].

But Yarm was the greatest sufferer as it was to be on many subsequent occasions (Fig 2.2). The river bank was overtopped in the early hours of 17 February, as was graphically recounted in a letter from Mr M. Johnson of Magdalen College, Oxford, to Dr Birch[15]:

It came into Yarm, throwing down all the garden and orchard walls that obstructed its passage and forcing its way through the windows of houses in the middle of the street, which the people who were aware of it readily encouraged lest otherwise the whole house might fall. Those who perceived it coming immediately got boats and took the people whose houses were low, out of their windows and waked the town. The alarm presently made them sensible of their danger and some had the good fortune to save their horses which would otherwise have drowned in the stables, by bringing them upstairs into their houses. The flood continued until eleven o'clock in the morning at which time the water was five and a half feet deep in the lower apartments and the people got into their uppermost rooms where they had the melancholy prospect of a perfect sea in the street, with horses, cows, sheep, hogs and all manner of household goods floating. About this time there was a great cry for provisions and they got some from the neighbouring villages that had not suffered but not near sufficient.

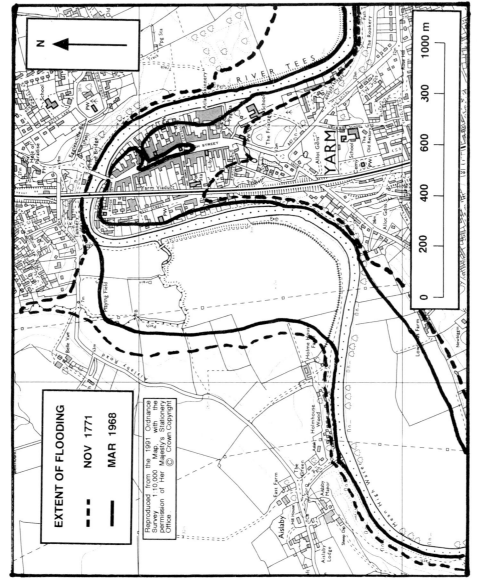

Fig 2.2 The town of Yarm encircled by the river Tees showing the extent of flooding in 1968 and 1771.

EXTENT OF FLOODING

---- NOV 1771

——— MAR 1968

Reproduced from the 1991 Ordnance Survey 1:10,000 Map, with the permission of Her Majesty's Stationery Office. © Crown Copyright

There was one thing rather comical than otherwise happened in the midst of this doleful spectacle. A sow big with young had swum until her strength was quite exhausted; a wheelbarrow was carried by the torrent out of somebody's yard which the sow being pretty near, laid her nose and forefeet into and suffered herself to be carried by the flood till she got safe to land.

They found the flood abated very fast and six hours later it was entirely gone. I went to see the town the next day; the people of all ranks were busy cleaning their houses and airing them. The poor people who had but one room below stairs were entirely ruined, and those who had shops and granaries were much damaged. They made a handsome collection round about for the poor, and the loss of the merchants is computed at £3000. One great happiness is that no one lost their lives.

Various other accounts differ in respect of the depth of water in the houses 'near eight feet high in several houses' and 'near six feet deep at the Cross which is the highest part of the whole town'. Richardson[16] notes that the Tees touched the covering of the Shambles that stood in the main street.

BRITAIN'S FIRST FLOOD WARNING SERVICE

Before the great flood of 1771 there were four further occasions when the river entered Yarm. However, in each case the damage was moderated by the timely intervention of a divine, the Rev. Bramwell of Hurworth.

The first of these incidents was on 12 October 1761, and the *Gentleman's Magazine* refers to the overflowing of Yarm but states that 'the event being foreseen the danger was provided against and no considerable damaged ensued'. The Stockton ferry was driven from its moorings and lost, and two other ships, one a sloop laden with wheat, were driven out to sea.

The floods of December 1763, when the river rose twice within the month, were more serious. The churchwarden's accounts for the parish church in Yarm in December 1763 cover payment for cleaning the church and setting up the churchyard wall after 'the first and second floods'. A correspondent from Yarm writes to the *Newcastle Journal*:

We have this Day had a prodigious Flood of Water in many places of the Street and also in several Houses it is about six feet high. Much damage is sustained by many of the inhabitants.

On the third of these occasions, on 8 Nov 1770, we learn further of the source of warning in a letter from Yarm to the *Newcastle Chronicle*. The writer takes the opportunity to moralise on the good works of the Rector:

The late rains swelled the Tees so that it entered the town (Yarm) and was two feet deep in many houses and would have done great damage had it not been for the Rev Mr Bramwell of Hurworth who is so happily situated on the said river, that he knows with exactness by the rising of the water, when there is danger, to what height it will rise in Yarm; and is able by sending express to give the inhabitants six or eight hours notice. This is the third time that Yarm is obliged to this gentleman for his kind intelligence. It would be well if his brethren, who are equally favoured with opportunities in being useful in social life would show the like good disposition. We should have no persecutions or prosecutions for the want of a conscientious conformity;– no litigation or altercation about the killing of a hare, a pheasant or a partridge but each man would be useful with the advantage he possessed.

A warning could only be given if the flood progressed more slowly on its meandering course than a horse could travel the more direct route. Present-day observations show that very large floods travel more slowly than smaller ones as they are delayed in spreading out across the floodplain. Figure 2.3. (p. 35). shows how flood travel time from Darlington (Broken Scar) to Yarm varies at different flows.

I have circulated information on this early flood warning amongst members of the British Hydrological Society but no one has yet claimed knowledge of an earlier warning service in Britain.

THE GREAT FLOOD OF 1771

The Rev. Bramwell again raised the alarm at Yarm for the flood of 17 November 1771 but this was of such extraordinary proportions that the precautions taken were quite inadequate. For this flood was by far the largest over the historic period not only on the Tees but also on the Wear and Tyne[17,18].

Surprisingly little is reported of the weather conditions which caused such a remarkable event. On the coastal area, rain began on Friday morning 15 November, accompanied by an north-east wind. It continued without break until the following night but was hardly of sufficient intensity to account for the severity of the flood. Pennine rainfall must have been much greater.

The record of the trail of damage down the valley is more complete than for any previous flood. In the upper reaches, the old Winch bridge across a gorge section near Low Force (said to be the earliest suspension bridge in Europe) was lifted from its moorings on the south side. A man had crossed the bridge only minutes before. This occurrence was said to show the suddenness of the event; it could also demonstrate the foolhardiness of the traveller. At Low Houses, near Newbiggin, the fields were flooded to a considerable depth. At Middleton all the riverside grounds at Step Ends and Leekwath were covered and there was a lake-like expanse nearly all the way to Eggleston. At Mickleton the water extended from Ornella to Yarkers Lane[19].

At Barnard Castle the level began to rise at 4 p.m. on Saturday and within a couple of hours it had already risen to such an unusual level that people in the lower part of the town began to move goods from their houses. Towards evening the bridge opening became inadequate and the water spilled over and broke down the retaining wall on the Startforth side and took its course along the street. At the height of the flood people could touch the water with their hands over the bridge parapet. The causeway approach to the southern end of the bridge was torn up and the soil washed away, down to the level of the rock. After the flood, pedestrians had to descend from the bridge on ladders, a height of twelve feet. The turnpike gate was removed and the gatekeeper escaped with the loss of all his furniture.

Eight houses were demolished on the Startforth side adjacent to the bridge: some had not one stone left. On the north side, from the bridge to Thorngate Wind, workhouses, dry-houses and tanyards were left in ruins. A short distance below the town, a corn mill with outhouses and stables belonging to Lord

Darlington was swept away. The official list of sufferers had twenty-one householders from Barnard Castle, fifteen of whom lost all furniture and possessions. There were no lives lost but it was a close call for a certain John Wright, a woolcomber:

In his anxiety to secure his stock in trade he ascended to an upper room and then found his retreat cut off. He was frantic in his discovery and his fears were heightened on hearing the fall of an adjacent house. At length he resigned himself to his fate and stretching on his woolpacks fell fast asleep in which condition he was found by his friends. His escape was providential for a part of the dwelling fell an hour or two after it was vacated.

In retrospect the event was not without humour and even profit for a certain dyer who had to beat a hurried retreat from his cellars where he had a few pieces of tammies in a kettle, receiving their last process. When the waters had subsided he returned to the kettle and found it filled with sand and mud which, when removed, revealed goods which had 'attained a colour beyond his most sanguine expectations'. The articles were sent to London and gave such satisfaction that orders were forwarded for a further supply of the same shade. However the dyer, no longer assisted by the genius of the river, failed in every attempt to produce it.

Downstream from Barnard Castle the Tees is joined by the river Greta, a principal tributary. It too was in full spate and all its bridges were carried away: at Gilmonby and Rutherford and Greta bridge which now carries the A66.

Below the Greta confluence at Wycliffe, the miller had to retreat to the highest room of his house. He lost three horses. At Barforth the farmer lost a brood mare, seven sheep and two stacks of hay, and across the river the turnpike road (now the A67) east of Winston was washed away for a hundred yards. Through Gainford the water carried away part of the churchyard along with coffins and corpses, some of which were deposited eight miles downstream at Blackwell. The waulk mill at Piercebridge was driven down.

Below this point the flood began to spread out to the full width of the floodplain. At Low Conniscliffe the river was half a mile wide, and levelled hedges, uprooted trees and spread gravel and boulders to more than one foot depth over a wide area. William Allison, at Oxen-le-Fields, had water six feet deep in his house. Several horses drowned in the stables but one huge draught horse swam into a pear tree and was found next morning supported in the branches.

At Croft the flood overtopped the bridge and carried away about thirty yards of the bridge parapet next to the turnpike gate, which was also torn down. The bridge itself survived. The church gates were also removed and the water entered the church to a depth of three feet six inches. Many houses were flooded and the *Newcastle Chronicle* of 30 November 1771 records the following endearing story:

At Croft a man and his wife were forced to the top of their house. They clung by the rigging tree a long time; but at last the old woman being no longer able to bear herself up, took leave of her husband and dropt down: on which the husband out of lasting affection replied, 'No, my dear, as we have lived forty years happily together, so let us die in peace and love', and instantly leaving his hold, resigned himself to the will of Providence. However as it happened, the upper floor of the house remained standing and they were rescued when the waters subsided.

Two loops of the river further downstream, the inhabitants of Neasham 'lost their all'. The bridge was badly damaged. Two arches were cracked from top to bottom and the foundations of another arch totally destroyed.

From his look-out at Hurworth the Rev. Bramwell sensed the danger early on Saturday evening and sent his servant off in haste to Yarm. He arrived there at 8.30 p.m. and informed the residents that they could expect very high water at three in the morning; but, as the waters were still rising when he left Hurworth, he could not ascertain just how high it would be in Yarm. At that time the Yarm level was not much above normal and, although the Crossbell was rung, the residents were fairly leisurely in their reparations. But the river rose so rapidly that many had to leave shops and warehouses before their goods were properly secured. By midnight the water was ten feet deep in the streets. When the flood reached its peak at eight o'clock on Sunday morning, the water was fifteen feet deep and every house was deeply submerged. The flood level is recorded on a plaque on the south wall of the Town Hall.

The arches of the bridge were full so that the water made its way over the battlements, 'the greater part being driven back with a dreadful torrent down the west side of the town'. All the garden walls from Flapper Street to Bentley Wind were thrown down. Remaining residents retreated first to their upper rooms and then, as the water rose, to their rooftops. Public-spirited neighbours from Stockton brought two boats overland by carriage and rescued thirty or forty people. One woman, Ann Richardson, had sat fifteen hours on top of a house with a child in her arms, and almost starved to death before she was rescued. In all seven people were drowned.

The Shambles and six dwelling houses were entirely demolished and many others were rendered uninhabitable. The water was 'above nine feet deep' in the church. The pulpit was overturned and the pews were afloat. Trade was devastated. Even those who had taken precautions only moved their goods a foot or so above the watermark of the 1753 flood, but this level was exceeded by five feet eight inches. A charitable fund was quickly established by the local gentry and merchants, and held by Mr Carter, treasurer of Yarm. This was for the relief of poorer folk 'whose losses were estimated to total £1588.7s.0d, although the total losses were of the order of £7000'. It is pleasing to note that the value of Rev. Bramwell's flood warning service was recognised: the servant was paid half a guinea for coming twice to Yarm 'to give account of the water'.

In the tidal reach downstream from Yarm, damage was limited, with only one warehouse and two or three liquor cellars flooded in Stockton.

VICTIMS OF THE TEES WAVE
The characteristic of the Tees to rise very rapidly in level has already been mentioned. This can occur not only in major floods but even when the river

stays within its banks. The Tees wave may spell disaster for those unfortunate enough to be caught in mid-channel.

This happened, for example on New Year's Eve 1790 when a party of young people from Middleton was returning home from a celebration in Baldersdale[19]. They found the river swollen and the ford at Step Ends opposite the town impassable. They sought an alternative crossing at Leekwath half a mile downstream which, because of the width of the channel, was generally safer. But that too seemed dangerous and, with one exception, they resolved to take the long road home via Eggleston bridge. However, Joseph Forster rashly attempted the crossing in spite of his companions' protestations, and they watched him, spellbound, in the dim moonlight as he struggled against the current. He had got about two-thirds of the way across when, confident of his success, he turned and waved his handkerchief. But his triumph was premature, for 'just at that instant the flood suddenly rose higher and became more impetuous – as if a great reservoir had burst – and he was struck down, engulfed, and never seen alive again'. It was seven months before his body was found far downriver at Gainford.

Similar occurrences were reported from time to time. In September 1821 two young people from West Layton were crossing the ford at Wycliffe Sills when they were overwhelmed by a sudden rush of the 'well-known Tees wave' and were both drowned[20]. On 16 December 1833 the Tees was reported to rise 'with great rapidity to an unusual height'. A labourer, attempting to secure timber at New bridge Blackwell, was swept away with his timber. He was observed as he was swept under Croft bridge and rescued at Hurworth by boat.

In 1842, after a summer thunderstorm, the Tees 'came down in an unusual body of water at one sweep'. Some dyers rinsing yarn for carpet manufacture had a narrow escape but there was considerable loss of livestock.

On 30 December 1924 the Tees rose twelve feet in forty-five minutes. Women workers had to be rescued from Croft Mill and sixty-eight sheep were drowned on the haugh land in the same locality. Two years later on 20 September 1926, the river rose ten feet in thirty minutes at Darlington.

In recent decades, with the growth in the number of reservoirs in the upper reaches of the Tees catchment holding back part of the flow, the tendency for rapid rise has decreased. However, there is still much danger for the unwary angler and river user.

A CENTURY OF FLOODS

The flood level of 1771 exceeded anything that has occurred since then, but there were numerous occasions in the following century when riparian property was inundated. The patience of many riverside householders must have been sorely tried. In several instances the only available information is for Yarm but other villages upstream must have been similarly affected.

The churchwardens' accounts at Yarm refer to floods in 1783 and 1789, with no further details as to the extent. However, flooding in the church implies that much other property was affected. The *Newcastle Chronicle* of 1 September 1792 refers to a great swell in the Tees when the water flowed to a considerable height 'in the town'. The town is not identified, but was again probably Yarm.

Flooding originated from an unusual source in 1794. The winter that year was very severe and the ground was covered with snow almost continuously from Christmas Eve to the latter part of March. There was a temporary break-up of ice in the lower reaches of the river on 11 February, and the obstruction caused by the ice floes raised the level at Stockton by seven or eight inches higher than it reached in 1771. Warehouses were badly affected and blocks of ice left on the carrs presented the appearance of a frozen sea.

An unusually high tide was probably the main reason for the next flooding in the lower reaches of the river in 1809, although there was also said to be a 'great fresh' in the river. The sea bank at Haverton Hill was breached and the works to straighten the river between Portrack and Stockton were delayed when water broke into the cut. At Stockton race-course, flooded by the Tees, it is reported that horses ran belly-deep in water – which says much for the persistence of punters, jockeys and horses.

Great but unspecified damage was reported on the Tees on the occasion of a major snowmelt flood on the Tyne in 1815. But in the next big winter flood in 1822 there was no snow. The weather through January 1822 had been unusually mild and the ground was quite dry in the lowlands at the onset of a severe south-westerly gale and heavy rainfall in the Pennines. The banks were again overtopped at Croft and the battlements of Croft bridge were damaged. Yarm was said to have had the highest flood since 1783. There the level began to rise at 9 p.m. on Saturday 2 February and continued its advance through the night till 10 a.m on Sunday when it was seven feet deep in many parts of the main street. It had been a moonlit night and many of the residents, who had received a warning, spent it removing their property to upper rooms. In the morning 'the Vale of Tees had become an immense smooth silver lake in which boats were plying, and in the midst of which the town of Yarm seemed immersed'.

The flood of 13 July 1828 appears to have been comparatively small, but its occurrence in the summer caused considerable agricultural loss. The autumn flood of the following year was much more serious, especially in the upper reaches where it was comparable to that of 1771. It covered much of the lowlands below Middleton on the morning of 14 October 1829. Two men on their way to work saw that Ornella Farm was surrounded and ran down to rouse the residents. The children of the household, who were sleeping upstairs, recalled long afterwards the frantic shouts of their father, 'Get up! Get up! We are all going to be drowned!' They leapt from bed and, looking out of their window, saw the vast expanse of water so covered with spray and foam (whipped up by the storm force north-easterly winds) that it looked like snow. Not far away at Collingwood the flood rose waist high in the corn mill. There the household were alerted by one of the family who had stayed up to tend an ailing animal and had been startled by a strange splashing noise. Several houses were deeply flooded at Barnard Castle, especially at Bridgegate where some houses had been rebuilt since 1771. It was four feet eight inches deep in Mr Crampton's house at the south end of the bridge and he, with others, had furniture and clothing washed away. A new stone bridge under construction at Whorlton was swept away and the work had to be abandoned. The effects of the storm diminished downstream and the water was a mere six feet deep in Yarm High Street (less than it had been in 1822).

The next notable event occurred on 10 January 1837 when a rapid thaw disposed of the heavy snowfall accumulated over Christmas. A new wooden bridge was carried away at Sockburn on the narrow southern loop of the river downstream from Neasham and a great many houses were inundated at Yarm. The flood of 29 September 1852 was unusual in that it appears to have originated mainly in the lower parts of the catchment with serious flooding of the Skerne. There was some flooding at Croft and Neasham but no indication of problems at Yarm.

An event similar in magnitude and origin occurred four years to the day later (28 September 1856). There were no reports of property flooded along the Tees but much agricultural land was immersed, and cattle, corn and timber were carried downstream. One of the sheaves and stacks of wheat floating past Stockton had a rather agitated man perched on top. He had been attempting to secure the stack near Yarm when the water rose too rapidly for him to escape. A boat was put out and he was rescued near the chain bridge.

Shortly afterwards, on 8 December 1856, the river was up again, this time sufficiently to dampen the citizens of Yarm. The warning bell was sounded at four in the morning and many of the residents of Bridge Street stepped from bed into water which had already entered their houses. The water continued to rise until midday and boats ferried provisions down the streets of the town. Four hours later the water had nearly all gone.

Thirteen years passed before flooding again affected Yarm. This was a snowmelt flood at an unusually early date, 13 November 1869. Heavy snow had fallen on Wednesday 9. The thaw followed quickly from Friday onward, accompanied by a strong westerly wind and heavy rain. Effects were most notable in the upper reaches. At High Force the central rock which normally projects high above the water level was almost completely immersed. Winch bridge was slightly overflowed and water ran more than three feet deep past its southern end. At Middleton bridge the level was high enough to pour through the spandrel openings and the masonry of the north abutment was damaged. At Barnard Castle the flood rose to the floor level of Mr Crampton's house at the south end of the bridge. Near Darlington a temporary bridge, belonging to the Merrybent railway company, at the site of the present A1(M) bridge, was carried off. On Sunday at Yarm the Tees covered the garden walls adjacent to the river and the High Street, flooding a number of houses.

Two further floods followed in the 1870s. On Good Friday 29 March 1872, the combination of rain and thaw again caused the river to overflow at Yarm. The engine room in the paper mill was flooded first, then low-lying houses and gardens. Occupants of the High Street, observing the flood from their upper windows, were provided with a little diversion when some amateur anglers caught a fish which had appeared at the door of the newsagent. It was a trout weighing about one-and-a-half pounds. In the autumn of 1875 there were two floods in quick succession which mainly affected the river Skerne, but also caused some damage in the lower reaches of the Tees. In the smaller of these, Wren's paper mill at Yarm was again affected and the water stopped the engines for a couple of hours but it barely reached street level. The flood which followed on 14 November 1875 was more noteworthy. At Croft the Tees overflowed the road. From the croquet grounds to the baths was a sheet of water two to three feet deep. At the bridge the river overtopped the banks on both sides and ground floors were inundated. Yarm High Street was again covered to several feet and in some houses water was five feet deep. The gasworks were flooded. The morning church services in Yarm were curtailed and the evening ones were cancelled.

SNOW STORM AND FLOOD – THE WINTER OF 1881

The floods at the end of the remarkable winter of 1881 were the culmination of a century of floods. They also mark a turning point in the potential for flooding, and the Tees has never again experienced a flood of this magnitude. Man-made changes to the river channel and catchment which had begun in the early nineteenth century now developed apace and made the recurrence of such an event a much more remote possibility. These changes are described in the next section.

The winter of 1880/1 was prolonged as well as severe[21]. First snows were reported in October but the principal storms occurred around 13 January and 3 to 5 March. January was also intensely cold; by mid-month the Tees had frozen at Stockton and at one time a thousand people were said to have gone skating at Middlesborough's Albert Park. Partial thaws occurred in the lowlands but had little effect in upper Teesdale where, by early March, drifts lay twenty feet deep. A slow thaw started on Sunday 6 March but early on Wednesday the wind veered west, strengthened, and temperatures increased dramatically. The river rose rapidly at first during the morning and continued to rise steadily through much of the day.

In the middle and upper reaches many footbridges were carried away, including those over the Tees at Middleton and Cotherstone, and over the Balder, close to its confluence with the Tees. At Barnard Castle, a crowd assembled to enjoy the spectacle in the bright spring sunshine between the showers. Their interest was concentrated on Thorngate footbridge. Although this wrought-iron bridge had been opened only ten years before, its stability was uncertain. In its 180-foot length it had two iron piers in the channel, but the one on the Durham side was not firmly fixed to the rock. With the rising waters during the morning came tree trunks and other debris which, with the force of the water, detached the pier completely so that it hung loose from the bridge deck which now began to oscillate alarmingly. Even at this stage some of the onlookers continued to cross. But, at precisely twelve minutes before midday, a crack was heard, loud above the roar of the seething river. The bridge parted in the centre, rolled over and was swept away in halves, not a vestige of the fabric remaining.

Two unfortunates, Richard Gargett a gamekeeper and William Thwaites a watchmaker, had advanced only a pace or so on to the Durham side of the bridge, but the destruction was so swift and complete that escape was impossible. They were carried off with the structure and drowned. Thwaites rose twice to the surface with the movement of the bridge and was seen holding on grimly to the lattice work. He floated in the boiling current for over two hundred yards but was then washed over the mill weir and lost. Gargett appears to have been instantaneously engulfed.

Meanwhile, the river continued to rise and did not reach its peak until eleven o'clock in the evening. Ullathorne's shoe thread factory, upstream from the old bridge was under water, and houses beside the bridge were flooded. (Ullathorne's mill was demolished in the early 1980s, but the 1881 flood level is preserved on an engraved stone on the downstream side.) The road at the Sills was covered for some distance. The 'island' at the Flax mill was submerged. The water stood four-and-a-half feet deep in the buildings and the managers supervised the removal of materials until late into the night. Over twenty tons of sand were deposited in Rudd's steam corn mill.

Downstream, Wycliffe mill and Carlbury mill were flooded. Opposite High Conniscliffe the embankment was overtopped, flooding Holme House farm cottages. The boathouse at Cleasby was filled to window level and a mark showing the level of the flood in 1829 was exceeded by eight inches. The road from Stapleton to Blackwell bridge was impassable. At Oxen-le-Fields the resident, Mr Bamlett, 'was saved the trouble of putting out his fires'. It was said to be the first time the house had been flooded since 1815 and at that time it did not have bank protection.

Flooding at Croft was extensive. The banks were overtopped upstream on the Yorkshire side and the waters rushed into the village from Monkend. The Rectory was surrounded, the school penetrated and the basement of Spa Hotel flooded. At the other end of the bridge the water was four or five feet deep on the road and was into houses up to the Comet Inn. Some men from the village managed to rescue one of the main beams from Step Ends bridge from Middleton as it floated past. It was converted into a village seat and stood for several decades near Croft bridge as a memorial to the occasion.

A bridge was swept down at Pilmore and many farms were flooded between Croft and Yarm. At Neasham only five of the sixty houses in the village escaped. Yarm again suffered badly, the water being as much as eight feet deep in some parts of High Street, flooding church and chapel, shops and warehouses. It was five feet deep at the Town Hall where a plaque, 1.66 metres below that of the 1771 flood, commemorates the event.

Floods are short-lived and details of timing and level usually fade quickly from the memory. Often the date and year of a flood thirty years ago cannot be remembered to within a decade unless there are some associated events to act as *aides memoires*. The memory of Rev. Ridley Verity must hold a record for length and accuracy. He was seven years old at the time of the flood and was interviewed in 1962. He recalled how the river began to rise on Wednesday 9 March 1881. It rose so quickly that the congregation at the Lenten service had to leave the church hurriedly. That evening the maid took him outside to see the water playing like fountains above the gullies. Next morning the river had risen to its peak and the whole household were confined to the first floor rooms with nothing to eat except birthday cake, it being his mother's birthday. He saw boats passing along the High Street and the maid called to the boatman to bring milk for his baby brother. To while away the time, he launched paper ships from the fifth stair of the house. The level of the fourth stair was later surveyed and found to be entirely consistent with the level recorded at the town hall. On Friday morning the water level had receded leaving behind masses of silt and ooze.

Observers along the river looked back to 1829 to find a flood of comparable magnitude. In 1881 the flood at Barnard Castle was said to be eleven inches lower than in 1829 but at Cleasby, Oxen-le-Fields, Croft and Yarm, evidence suggests that the later event was the larger. This contrast between upstream and downstream conditions is quite possible. In 1881, with a thaw occurring simultaneously over the whole catchment, both upland and lowland tributaries were in spate, whereas the autumn rainfall storm of 1829 was concentrated in the Pennines.

Floods of 1753, 1783 and 1822 reached similar heights to that of 1881 at some points along the river, but only the flood of 1771 was unequivocally higher throughout its length. However, the 1.66m difference in peak level at Yarm may not do justice to the 1881 flood, as changes had occurred downstream which enabled the channel to carry a greater flow for a given level.

A NEW REGIME – DREDGING AND RESERVOIRS

The principal man-made changes in the river have been designed to solve problems of navigation and water supply but these measures have gradually alleviated flooding as much as those designed primarily for flood protection.

Works in the estuary to improve navigation began early in the nineteenth century[22]. Previously passage up the river for vessels had been a slow process as there was no clear channel. At low tide broad banks of sand and gravel were exposed and the channel depth below Stockton could be as little as two feet. Above Stockton the conditions were even more restricting and it often took four tides for the journey to Yarm, which was still vying with Stockton as the major port of the Tees. In addition to sand shoals there were the obstacles of Old Roger Rock and the shallow Rifle Butts reach.

Various proposals to improve navigation were made in the late eighteenth century but the first major step was taken with the Act of Parliament of 1808 which created the Tees Navigation Company. The Company was given the power to 'dig, cut through, blast or otherwise to remove or destroy all or any of the rock, shoals, shallows, mud and sand banks and other obstructions'. The first task was to make a cut across the narrow neck of the Mandale Loop between Stockton and Portrack, shortening the river by two-and-a-half miles in 1810. A second cut from Portrack to Newport in 1828 shortened the distance by a further three-quarters of a mile.

Dredging commenced in the mid-1820s but progress was slow until 1852 when the T.N.C. was dissolved and the Tees Conservancy Commission was set up. Between 1854 and 1877 seven million tons of material were removed, and thereafter for several decades dredging settled down to a steady rate of 400,000 to 500,000 cubic yards per year. Work was concentrated mainly in the lower reaches of the estuary to improve navigation to Stockton but some clearance was also carried out further upstream. Old Roger Rock near Preston was blasted out in 1850 and Fowler records that in 1862 an additional one foot in depth was secured over the 'Yarm Schoal'. By this stage, however, Yarm had virtually ceased to be a port.

The combined effect of these changes on flood levels is uncertain but it is likely to have been greatest in the upper reaches of the estuary. It is quite possible that, for a given flood flow at Yarm, the level is now two feet lower.

The second major change has been at higher elevations of the catchment where a series of reservoirs has been built to meet the needs of a growing population and the rapidly developing industrial demand for water[23]. Reservoired sub-catchments now cover a far greater proportion of the total Tees catchment than in any other major Northumbrian catchment: 22% of the area upstream from Darlington and 14% of the area above the tidal limit. They have been built in the wettest areas which normally contribute the most to floods.

The effect of reservoirs on flooding is twofold. When they are drawn down, as they commonly are during the summer months, they absorb the flood water and hence reduce the flood volume downstream. Even when they are full they delay the flood wave and reduce the peak, roughly in proportion to the reservoir surface area.

The first Pennine reservoir to be constructed was at Hury in 1894 and the last at Cow Green in 1970. The reservoirs have gradually reduced the flood potential of the Tees over the last hundred years. The sequence of reservoir construction, their capacities and catchment areas are shown in Table 2.1.

Table 2.1. Details of Teesdale Reservoirs

Name	Year of Completion	Dam Height	Capacity	Reservoir Area	Catchment Area
		metres	million cubic metres	Km²	Km²
Hury	1894	30	3.90	0.51	43.1
Blackton	1896	24	2.11	0.27	–
Grassholme	1915	33	6.06	0.57	78.7
Selset	1960	39	15.32	1.11	–
Balderhead	1965	48	19.67	1.17	–
Cow Green	1970	25	40.92	3.12	58.9

FROM 1881 TO 1950

Although there has been no event as severe as that of 1881, flooding of a lesser magnitude has continued. On at least seven occasions since then the water has flowed into Yarm High Street.

The first of these occasions was on 6 November 1886 when the Skerne and other lowland tributaries were more affected than the main Tees. Neasham was reported flooded 'to an enormous height' and at Yarm boats were used in the streets. A snowmelt flood followed on 25 January 1890. At Barnard Castle it was the highest since 1881; the roads at Croft and Neasham were covered but Yarm appears to have escaped.

The autumn of 1892 was unusual. The first snows arrived on 30 September and lay several inches deep on Mickle Fell. Thunderstorms brought heavy local rain two days later, sufficient to raise the Tees to moderately high levels but also to saturate the soil in advance of more widespread rain on 14 October. At Barnard Castle work was in progress on the pipe-crossing bridge near the mouth of the Deepdale beck. Scaffolding and a crane were overturned and dashed against the stone bridge two hundred yards downstream. At Neasham the road was impassable and several houses were flooded, whilst at Yarm the water lay three-and-a-half feet deep at some places in the High Street and flooded houses in High Church Wynd and Bridge Street and the Wesleyan Sunday School[24]. The centre of the heaviest rainfall was further south and the river Ouse at York rose to its highest level since 1831.

The Tees escaped the worst of the regional storm of October 1900 but in the similar floods three years later (the worst of this century on the Wear), the Tees and its tributaries did not escape. The High Street in Yarm was flooded for the first time since 1892. Work at the skin yard had to stop when the water reached the engines. The worst effects, however, were felt in North Yorkshire along the Leven and the small becks draining through Middlesborough.

Over the next decade there was no flooding in the Tees as was the case in other northern rivers, and it was January 1918 before the papers found the state of the river worth comment amongst the more momentous events of Europe. In the last winter of the Great War, bitter winds from the east blew across Europe. The German army was regrouping behind the Hindenberg line for its last desperate push to dislodge the Allies and deal a decisive blow before the fresh American army could make its presence felt. Snow drifted across the trenches and soldiers froze to death. The cold extended to northern England and temperatures in mid-January dipped to $-17°C$. The rivers froze and snow drifted to more than fifteen feet deep in upper Teesdale. The thaw came with heavy rain on 21 January and the resulting flood in the upper reaches was not far short of 1881. At its peak at 4 a.m. the Tees in Barnard Castle was within a foot of the 1881 mark on Ullathorne's Flax Mill where 'the floors had risen up out of their places'. By 5.30 a.m. the water was lashing the walls of the boathouse cottage close to the bridge at Stapleton and when it reached its highest there at 11 a.m. the hedgerows were almost completely submerged. At Blackwell Hall the level was just four inches below that of 1881. However, unusually for a winter snowmelt flood, the high levels did not persist long. As is normal with such short-lived events the flood spent much of its energy on the floodplain and, without replenishment from lowland rivers, the effect downstream was reduced. There was flooding at Croft, Neasham and Yarm but, by the time it reached its peak at Yarm at 7 p.m., it was just two feet deep in Yarm High Street.

A succession of floods followed in the mid–1920s. None of these was of exceptional magnitude but on seven occasions at least the river overflowed roads and houses at Croft and Neasham. It entered the lower parts of Yarm only on 30 December 1924 when a large pool collected at the north end of the High Street. The dates of the floods were:

13	November	1923
1	June	1924
30	December	1924
20	September	1926
15	August	1927
21	September	1927
13	June	1928

Five of these occurred in summer and some of them were locally intense. The rapid rise in level of the 'Tees wave' of September 1926 has already been mentioned. The storm of 15 August 1927 was severe in the upper Tees and the waterfall at High Force was spectacular where it covered the whole central rock (Plate 2.3). At Middleton the water poured through the bridge spandrel holes for the first time (it was said) since 1881. In the flood of November 1923, a

Plate 2.3 The river Tees in full spate at High Force in August 1927 with flow on both sides of the central rock, rarely repeated after the construction of Cow Green in 1970.

rabbit was observed emulating the exploits of the heroes of Watership Down but with a less fortunate outcome. It was seen at Neasham 'perilously perched on a long branch of a tree which was being carried along by the swirling waters. The log was drawn ashore and the bunny, rescued from his unhappy plight only, it is stated, to meet a death more ignominious than that which would have been his fate had he continued his watery adventure.'

The next flood was possibly the worst of the twentieth century but I have been unable to find a single contemporary written description. During World War II reference to meteorological or hydrological extremes was forbidden even in retrospect and information is derived from personal recollections of longtime residents of Yarm as recounted to Riby in 1979[25].

High Church Wynd on the west side of High Street was usually one of the first places affected and Elizabeth Quency remembered that she had water in her house twice. Her father had to wade up the Wynd to the High Street to catch his bus to work at half past six in the morning. The second time it rose to the second stair, and she had to live upstairs for two days before she could get the place dried out and cleaned. That was in 1940 and soldiers were in the drill hall in the Wynd (now the police station), as well as in the chapel in West Street – and that was flooded too. Her son, she recalled, used to bring the soldiers in a boat down the Wynd.

Stan Harrison living in the Wynd also remembers the 1940 flood. The family had a mill in Silver Street and were working until eleven o'clock getting all the 'stuff' upstairs. They stepped straight into 'Alf Garbutt's boat' and he rowed then into High Street and along Church Wynd. The water rose further and soldiers from the drill hall went across to his house where they lifted the family's piano on to the table. Mr Harrison is adamant that it was the only time during the family's period there that they actually had water in the house.

THE ERA OF RIVER MANAGEMENT

In 1950 regionally organised land drainage work commenced on the Tees, with the formation of the Wear and Tees River Board, and there followed a programme of river improvement and flood alleviation works. This work was taken over by the Northumbrian River Authority in 1965 and by Northumbrian Water Authority, with its wider responsibilities and powers, in 1974. It was again reorganised in 1989 and now falls within the control of the National Rivers Authority.

This is not to imply that there had been no previous river management or flood control works. Flood banks have existed in some reaches since at least the beginning of the nineteenth century. These were built by individual estate owners and farmers but, because they were discontinuous, the occupants often continued to suffer from incursions from unprotected reaches upstream. In the estuary the Tees Commissioners combined the construction of flood embankments to keep out river and sea, with the construction of training walls along the newly-dredged channel. Slag from the ironworks was used in the construction and the Commissioners were paid four pence per ton for its removal[25]. By 1880, twenty miles of training walls had been built between

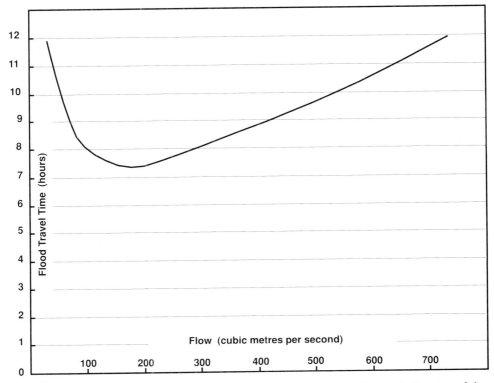

Fig 2.3 How travel time of a flood from Darlington to Yarm varies with the size of the flood.

Stockton and the sea. Upstream there was a more concentrated programme of bank building during World War I, with labour provided by prisoners of war.

Since the days of the River Board there has been a more co-ordinated approach, scientifically based on a growing body of data on river flow. The first gauging station on the river Tees was built at Broken Scar near Darlington in 1956 and over the next two decades the network built up to fourteen stations. With the associated network of raingauges, these flow measurement stations were (and are) used both for flood alleviation and for the planning and operation of water resources.

In addition to measuring flows at gauging stations, surveys of flood water levels along the course of the river became more thorough. Interviews with affected residents have also provided more detailed knowledge of the frequency and extent of flooding. Such improved information has enabled flood alleviation schemes to be planned in terms of the expected benefits. For example, it was found that some of the lowest-lying houses in Neasham were flooded about once every two years and the road as often as three times a year during the 1960s[26]. Work there received a high priority and a new flood embankment was built in 1970 which has kept village feet dry since that date.

Sometimes the problems were more complex. For example, at Croft and

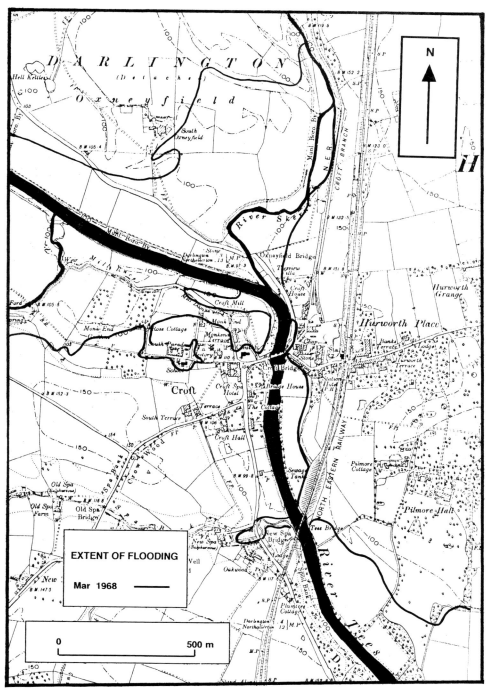

Fig 2.4 The villages of Croft and Hurworth Place showing the extent of flooding in March 1968.

Hurworth Place flooding resulted in part from the backing-up of flow by Croft bridge whose capacity was restricted by the oblique channel approach[27]. A further complication was the effects of the two tributary junctions of the Skerne and Clow beck (Fig 2.4). High flows in the Tees could back up these rivers, overflow their banks and provide alternative routes to flooding in the villages (Plate 2.4). Because of the difficult hydraulic conditions, a scale model of the river was built at the University of Newcastle upon Tyne to enable alternative improvement schemes to be tested[28]. The scheme finally selected involved a combination of channel realignment to give a smoother approach to the bridge and the raising of flood embankments and walls. The scheme was completed in 1979.

Two major schemes are currently being planned or built in the tidal reach of the Tees. The most notable change will be upstream from the new river Tees barrage to be constructed at Stockton. Its objective will be to improve the amenity and quality of the river upstream from the barrage by maintaining a steady level and by restricting the movement of contaminated tidal waters inland. There is a danger that such a scheme could also exacerbate flooding, especially at Yarm, although the operating policy for the barrage gates will be designed to minimise such problems.

However, plans for the alleviation of flooding at Yarm had already been in preparation since the mid-1980s, and it was possible to incorporate the effects of the barrage in the design brief for the Yarm flood alleviation scheme. At the

Plate 2.4 Flooding at Croft-on-Tees 6 March 1963, a fairly common occurrence before the construction of Teesdale reservoirs and flood protection at Croft. Photo. North of England Newspapers.

Plate 2.5 Unprecedented flooding at Brignall Mill farm during the Hurricane Charlie floods of 26 August 1986. *Photo. E. Ryle-Hodges.*

Plate 2.6 Yarm High Street during the flood of March 1968. *Photo. Northern Echo.*

time of writing (early 1992) the construction of the Yarm flood scheme is well under way. A particular emphasis is being placed on the sensitive use of materials and designs to blend with the historic buildings of the town.

RECENT FLOODS (1950-1992)

Compared with many historic floods, those of the last four decades have been minor but there have been memorable features. Records from gauging stations give precise information on levels reached and provide a basis for putting them in rank order. These records confirm the suspicion from earlier observations that the highest upstream floods are not always the biggest downstream.

The flood which reached the highest level at Broken Scar gauging station resulted from the aftermath of Hurricane Charlie on 26 August 1986. The area worst affected was south of the Northumbrian area in the Swale catchment but many rainfall stations in the Tees catchment recorded over 90 mm in twenty-four hours with the highest figure of 115 mm at Bar Gap farm near Bowes. The River Greta – not usually noted for its floods – was probably at its highest level since 1771. In its steep channel it carried along boulders of enormous size, lifted farm bridges, and swept through the farmyard of Brignall Mill, a site which no previous flooding had approached (Plate 2.5). On the main Tees, the embankments at Croft and Neasham proved effective. Compared with many winter floods this event was of short duration and the flood spent itself on the floodplain and did not top the banks at Yarm. However, fisherman John Leonard lost his life there when the dinghy he was using to transfer from his moored cabin cruiser overturned.

On 23 March 1968 100 mm of rain fell on melting snow on the upper part of the catchment. The resulting flood was more prolonged and of greater volume than that of 1986 but the peak level was 0.1 m lower at Broken Scar. In the headwaters a walker was drowned attempting to cross the Maize Beck. Croft and Neasham (as yet without their flood protection schemes) suffered badly. Thirty houses at Croft and Hurworth Place and half-a-dozen properties in Neasham were flooded. At Neasham Post Office the water was halfway up the counter. At Yarm, floodwaters entered the town along the wynds and closes and formed a pool half a metre deep in places in the High Street (Plate 2.6), stranding many cars.

Snowmelt flooding was also nationally widespread in January 1982. Fortuitously it occurred just after I had published a research paper in the *Journal of the Institution of Civil Engineers* drawing attention to the potential severity of floods resulting from snowmelt[29]. On the Tees the levels continued high for nearly two days and water covered much low-lying land in the lower reaches, and Yarm only just escaped.

Whilst the potential for really serious flooding on the Tees has diminished and embankments provide a good measure of protection, there is no doubt that the river can still unleash its power on riverside villages. The level of the flood mark of 1771 on Yarm town hall is a solemn reminder of past extremes, and the warning bell, which still lies silent inside, may again ring out the doleful news to the inhabitants.

REFERENCES

1. Ekwall, E. *English River-Names*, (Oxford, 1968)
2. Longstaffe, W. H. D. *History and Antiquities of Darlington*, (Stockton, 1854, reprinted 1973)
3. Page, W. (ed) *Victoria History of the County of York, North Riding*, quoting from Cal. Pat. 1354-8, (London, 1914)
4. Surtees, R. *The History and Antiquities of the County Palatine of Durham*, (4 vols., London, 1816-40), vol. 3, 408
5. Atkinson, J. C. (ed) Quarter Sessions Records, North Riding Records Society, (London, 1889)
6. Durham County Quarter Sessions. Mss, Durham County Record Office
7. Brewster, J. *The Parochial History and Antiquities of Stockton upon Tees*, (Stockton, 1829, reprinted 1971)
8. Brewster, J. *op. cit.* Stock's Memoranda: Extracts from a memorandum book entitled: *An account of some remarkable things since the year of our Lord 1699 by me Robert Stock*
9. Hodgson, J. C. *op. cit,* 118. Extracts from The Diary of Christopher Sanderson (1910)
10. Sanderson, C. Diary. Mss. Gateshead Public Library
11. Ord, J. W. *The History and Antiquities of Cleveland*, (London, 1846)
12. Graves, J. G. *The History of Cleveland*, (Carlisle 1808, reprinted 1972)
13. Hodgson, J. C., *op. cit.* The Diary of Thomas Gyll
14. Richmond, T. *The Local Records of Stockton and Neighbourhood*, (Stockton, 1868)
15. Wardell, J. W. *A History of Yarm: An Ancient North Riding Town*, quoting from Bibliotheca Topographica Britannia, (1957)
16. Richardson, M. A. *Memorials of the Floods*.
17. Bell, J. *Account of floods 1815 and 1771*.
18. Garret, W. *Account of floods in 1815 and 1771*.
19. Bell, W. (ed.) 'Local recollections of floods in the Tees', *Lord Fitzhugh Magazine, (c.* 1880)
20. Close, A. W. M. Unpublished compilation of newspaper records, plus articles by the compiler. Darlington Public Library
21. Bousfield, J. *Pleasant Memories of Darlington and Neighbourhood*, (London, 1881)
22. Le Guillou, M. *A History of the Lower Tees, 1001-1975*, (Cleveland County Libraries, 1978)
23. Northumbrian Water Authority, The Water Act 1973, Section 24 Survey, (1978)
24. Batty, A. (ed.) *A Postcard from Yarm*, (Stockton Borough Council)
25. Riby, J. 'The Problem at Yarm'. Unpublished BSc. Project Report, Teesside Polytechnic, (1980)
26. Northumbrian River Authority. 'Preliminary investigation of floods at Neasham'. Unpublished Internal Report, (1969)
27. Northumbrian Water Authority. Croft flood protection scheme, Engineers report, (1976)
28. Novak, P. Report on Croft flood protection scheme, Model tests, (University of Newcastle upon Tyne, 1973)
29. Archer, D. R. 'Severe snowmelt runoff in northeast England and its implications', *Proc. Instn Civil Engineers*, pt 2, 71 (1981)

3. THE RIVER SKERNE

*The same day were all the fountains of the great deep
broken up, and the windows of heaven were opened and
the rain was upon the earth forty days and forty nights*
Genesis 7,11

The river Skerne, a north bank tributary of the Tees, is a lowland river over its entire length. The highest point in its catchment, west of Shildon, is only 222 metres above sea level. The catchment has extensive areas of very flat land adjacent to the main channel and tributaries (Fig 3.1). In their natural state these 'carrs', as they are called, were flooded nearly every winter and the land remained poorly drained throughout the year. The largest such area is in the middle reaches where the picturesque villages of Bradbury and Mordon stood on natural mounds overlooking Bradbury, Mordon and Preston carrs. The main line railway and the A1(M) motorway now cross this area on low embankments.

The main settlements in the catchment have, for the most part, avoided the damp lower ground, and the small towns of Shildon, Ferryhill and Sedgefield grew up on the catchment divide. Darlington in the lower reaches is by far the largest town and, in its rapid industrial growth in the nineteenth century, the developers unfortunately overlooked the natural tendency of the river to spread beyond its channel. As we shall see, they left a legacy of problems for the inhabitants and river engineers.

The Skerne is very different from the Tees in its climate and hydrology. Average annual rainfall over the catchment is only 640 mm compared with 1200 mm on the Tees above the Skerne confluence. A much smaller proportion of that rainfall reaches the river channel as flood flow because of the drier climate and the greater permeability of soils and bedrock. The soils away from the river remain comparatively dry through much of the year and are able to absorb most of the storm rainfall. Locally, especially on the west side of the catchment where the boulder clay cover is thinner, the water may penetrate to groundwater through joints and fissures in the Magnesian limestone, which underlies the greater part of the catchment. This further delays the appearance of rainfall in the river channel. Indeed, in dry years such as the early 1970s when groundwater levels were low, there was even a substantial outflow from the Skerne into the limestone. As a consequence, generally less than twenty percent of storm rainfall reaches the channel during floods compared with over sixty percent on the upper Tees.

Although the volume of flow is lower on the Skerne, the alluvial channel has adjusted in size to convey the flood volume typically carried. When there is

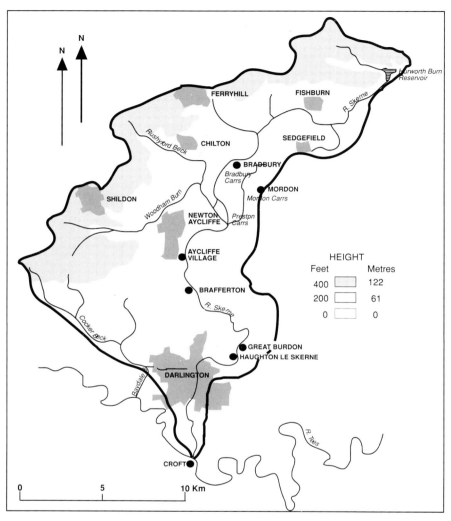

Fig 3.1 The river Skerne and its catchment

exceptional rainfall or snowmelt, especially on damp soils at the end of winter, the channel has insufficient capacity and flood water can spill out over a wide area.

EARLIEST RECORDS

There are no records of flooding on the Skerne before 1850. This is presumably because any flooding which did occur affected only the wet pastures on the floodplain and hardly excited comment. The first description to survive is a graphic account in the *Durham Advertiser* of a night journey on 29 September 1852 on the railway from Darlington to Durham, a line completed just eight years earlier.

North of Darlington a mile or two the line begins to traverse a dead level and for some miles the water was found standing for more than 100 yards on each side of the line, which passes across the plain on a slightly raised embankment. Bye and bye the rails became altogether submerged and the engine with its heavy toll of carriages slowly proceeded to clear the way through the immense lake one to two feet in depth. A brilliant moon shining through a clear frosty sky lighted up the inland sea, the train was thus strangely navigating and showed the water flashing through the wheels of the carriages as through the paddles of so many little land steamers. Only by the top of the hedgerows and trees arising out of the water could the passengers be convinced that the train was actually traversing an inland country and not an arm of the sea.

Four years later, on 29 September 1856, several hundred acres of land between Ferryhill and Aycliffe were flooded and the water came over the footboards of the rail carriages.

THE FLOODS OF 1875
The first year for which I have found a record of flooding of property on the Skerne was 1875, and in that year it occurred twice on a heroic scale. The first occasion was on 21 October after a day of continuous rain when an exceptional 60 millimetres was recorded. Flooding occurred from the gasworks at the upstream end to the park.

The water rose into the retort house of the gasworks and extinguished the white-hot retorts with great hissing and billowing of steam. The water eventually stood three feet deep in the gas yard and six feet deep in the purifying house. Twelve houses in John Street were flooded but the worst affected area was on the east bank from Freeman's Place to Victoria Road, where water was up to three feet deep. Two houses on the bridge at Parkgate were under water and one, a furniture dealer, had water coming through the kitchen window. A cellar of the Lord Nelson inn was flooded. A pet fox was drowned. The furnaces at Pease's Priestgate mills were put out. The *Northern Echo*, in lighter mood, reported:

In the neighbourhood of Park Street a well known character of Darlington was in bed on the ground floor. Probably a drop of the craythur had made him more than ordinarily somnolent. At any rate, he was oblivious to the flood, until finding one side cold he put down his hand and discovered it was wet. He turned over in astonishment, when lo and behold! the other side shared a similar fate. Leaping out of bed the unlucky fellow plunged bodily into the flood and as he phrased it became 'all o'er wet'.

One ingenious resident slowly worked his way up the street to dry land, by alternately placing one chair in front of the other.

Although this flood was, by general opinion, the worst in living memory, worse even than that of 1852 when the gasworks were unaffected, the residents and press faced it with detachment and humour. They were not to realise that it was merely a rehearsal for the full-scale performance three weeks later.

On Sunday 14 November there was 69 millimetres of rain over the twenty-four-hour period up to 8 p.m., not much greater than in October, but it fell on a catchment already saturated. Consequently more of the rain reached the river

43

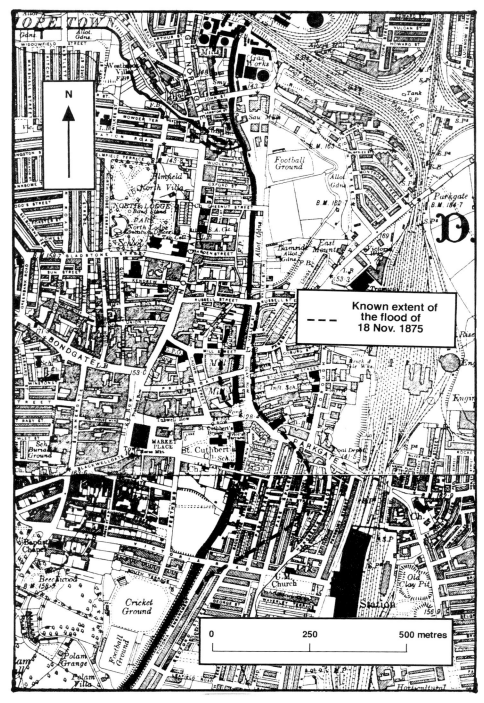

Fig 3.2 The course of the river Skerne through Darlington from the map of 1920 showing the known extent of the November 1875 flood.

and at its peak through Darlington the water level was eighteen inches to two feet higher than in the earlier flood.

In the middle reaches north of Aycliffe the water on Mordon carrs undermined the railway embankment for thirty feet and left the rails bridging the gap. Fortunately this was discovered before there was an accident. Several farm bridges were washed away, including the Middleham bridge, Island Farm bridges, Low Copelaw bridge and the Fourmart's bridge near Mainsforth[1].

In Darlington the water began to rise around nine o'clock on Saturday evening and rose quickly all through the night. By the morning, Skerne Row, Parkgate, Park Street, Park Place, Church Street, Bridge Street, Chapel Street, Swan Street, Backhouse Street, Model Place, Clay Row, Valley Street, Brunswick Street and the neighbourhood of Victoria Road were all under water (Fig 3.2). Along Houghton Road water stood five to ten feet deep in places. With the memory of the October flood still fresh in their minds, inhabitants spent the night taking whatever precautions were possible. However, many of those affected were poorer folk with only ground-floor rooms, and could only abandon their houses or beg shelter from their upstairs neighbours.

In the morning the mayor Edwin Pease and councillors appeared and made arrangements for evacuation of those worst affected.

Cabs ferried the victims to the Central Hall where blazing fires were lit. In the afternoon bread and coffee were supplied to nearly five hundred evacuees. The flood continued to rise until late afternoon and people began to prepare for a second night of discomfort. Some found beds in the workhouse but others, who steadfastly refused workhouse fare, preferred to sit up all night at the Central Hall.

The gasworks were more seriously affected than on the previous occasion. The manager had spent Saturday evening trying to build up temporary defences of timber and clay but by early morning his work was undone when his barricade was overtopped. The town remained in darkness for several days.

The town bridges were all submerged except Stone bridge and Victoria bridge. The latter formed a boundary between the lake, stretching southwards through South Park, and the canal-like streets to the north. A footbridge at North Lodge Gardens was washed away.

The Cocker beck tributary contributed to the disaster. At Cockerton the green below the School House was submerged and several houses were flooded. It ran in a torrent over Westbrook, across Northgate, and fully immersed the floor of the Baptist Chapel before joining forces with the Skerne.

By first light on Monday the floodwaters had receded from all the streets except Skerne Row and Backhouse Street but it was not until the afternoon that the cricket field, Polam Bottoms and Fleethams emerged, mud-smeared, from the waters.

THE LATE NINETEENTH CENTURY

After 1875 flooding on the Skerne was regularly recorded in the press. Usually this only affected agricultural land on the carrs, but sometimes water crept on to the roads and into houses in Darlington. Ten floods were reported between

1876 and 1903. It seems likely that there was a real increase in the incidence of flooding during this period, not simply greater awareness of the river's behaviour, probably resulting from an increase in frequency of heavy frontal rainfall combined with persisting high groundwater levels. As in other north-eastern rivers, flooding frequency again decreased markedly after 1903.

In 1876 the Corporation initiated work to improve the capacity of the channel downstream from Victoria Road bridge and to reduce ponding. When heavy rainfall occurred on two occasions that December (3 and 23), without serious flooding of property, the Corporation were quick to point to the value of their work. However, the Skerne did reach house level in Parkgate on 28 October 1880, and again on 6 November 1886, when water also got into John Street, Lambton Street and Clay Row.

The water also reached house level on 27 October 1900. On that occasion, Parkgate was impassable and in some houses and shops the furniture was afloat. Work at Brown's saw mill was suspended and the cellars of Pease's mill were inundated. Three years later, on 9 October 1903, the water reached the gasworks retorts for the first time since 1875 and the damage surpassed that of the 1900 flood. Flooding on the Cocker beck was particularly severe: the bridge at Cockerton was washed away and houses on the south side of the village were flooded. The whole of Clay Row was under water for 120 yards and could only be forded by horse traffic.

TWENTIETH CENTURY FLOODING

During the present century severe flooding seems to have been less frequent. From 1903 until the formation of the Wear and Tees River Board in 1950 I have found references in newspapers to only three Skerne floods. The first of these was on 1 June 1924 when the Skerne again overflowed Clay Row beside Priestgate mill. It was noted that the water level was within half an inch of Priestgate bridge despite the fact that the river had recently been straightened. Parkgate at the Haughton Road end was flooded. A lesser summer flood followed on 13 June 1928 with road flooding three to four feet in depth at Haughton Le Skerne. Minor flooding after a thaw was noted at Skerne bridge, Haughton, on 11 January 1948.

The incidence of minor flooding must have been far greater than records indicated for, in the second annual report of the Wear and Tees River Board in 1952, it was noted that representations had been made to the Board after the usual winter flooding at Haughton Road, Darlington (Plate 3.1). Top priority for surveys and improvement works was given to the Skerne[2].

Over the following fifteen years a comprehensive scheme in seven parts was surveyed, designed and executed, to alleviate flooding by improving the flood capacity of the Skerne. Work started at the confluence of the Tees and moved upstream to beyond Bradbury. The most difficult and expensive parts (Parts 2 and 3) covered the reach through Darlington from South Park to Great Burdon Bridge and commenced in 1954. Works were as follows.

1. The weir at the outlet to South Park lake was remodelled as a gauging weir and sluice gates were removed.

Plate 3.1 Haughton School, Darlington, November 1951. *Photo*. Evening Dispatch.

2. Russell Street weir was lowered by eighteen inches.
3. The channel at Five Arches bridge carrying the main railway was lined with sheet piles and deepened by an average of six feet.
4. From Five Arches bridge to Haughton road bridge the channel was much enlarged and a protective floodbank was constructed at Haughton School.
5. The troublesome Cocker beck was diverted into the Tees via the Baydale beck upstream of Cockerton and the Baydale channel was enlarged.

The seventh and final part of the Skerne Improvement Scheme – the regrading of the river and the raising and strengthening of the floodbanks from Bradbury to Holdsforth bridge – was completed by the Northumbrian River Authority in 1966.

Flooding along the length of the Skerne and through Darlington occurred in early March 1963 during a rapid thaw at the end of an extreme winter with more than two months' snow cover. However, in the year following the completion of the Improvement Scheme, the Skerne showed that it was not yet completely mastered.

Floods occurred on 17 October and 6 November 1967. In the first, twelve houses and several commercial premises were affected on Lambton Street Darlington. The wet ground conditions caused a greater proportion of the rainfall to run off during the second event, causing more serious flooding: fifty-four properties over a thirteen-acre area were affected. Industrial and commercial premises and houses were flooded in Valley Street, John Street, Leadenhall

47

Street, Oxford Street, Mount Street and Parkgate as well as Lambton Street. Haughton Church of England School went under to a depth of two feet. Although the measured flow in this event was about the same as in March 1963 the effects were rather more serious because of the laying of a sewer within the river channel and the road works adjacent to it. These caused obstructions to the flow. Large areas were again flooded on Bradbury, Preston and Mordon carrs.

Darlington Council had acquired and demolished riverside buildings between Chesnut Street and John Street and this made it possible for Northumbrian River Authority to enlarge the channel through Darlington again. The new works included a further lowering of the weir at Russell Street by two feet, and the widening of the channel between Chesnut Street and John Street from twenty-five to thirty-five feet with a reinforced concrete riverside wall on the west side. Between Cocker beck and Leadenhall Street there was no scope for widening but hydraulic conditions were improved by constructing a stream-lined channel with bed and banks paved with concrete. The works were carried out between 1970 and 1972.

Plate 3,2 Priestgate, Darlington, 29 March 1979. *Photo.* North of England Newspapers.

During the early 1970s the rivers of south-east Durham were quiescent but there was a definite change at the end of the summer drought of 1976. The drought was broken by an extraordinary deluge over the entire catchment when more than 100 mm of rain fell in forty-eight hours – an amount that could be expected on average only once in three hundred years (Fig 4.4). The very dry soil absorbed most of the rainfall and fortunately only about five percent of the water reached the Skerne immediately, so there was no significant flooding. However, this marked the beginning of a period of higher groundwater levels, wetter soils and a river and catchment which responded more readily to rainfall.

Over the next few years there were several floods which overtopped the embankments on agricultural land, including the prolonged rainfall flood between Christmas and New Year 1978 when the discharge at South Park gauging station matched that in 1963 and 1967. With one exception, these were now contained by the enlarged channel through Darlington.

The exception occurred in late March 1979. The winter had been characterised by a succession of severe snowstorms and thaws. An unusually late and heavy snowfall on 17 March had begun to melt on 25 March but the river was still swollen and the ground saturated or still snow-covered when forty to fifty millimetres of rain fell on 28 and 29 March. The proportion of rain reaching the river far exceeded that in any previous flood, and the peak flow through Darlington was fifty percent greater than in late 1978 (60 cumecs compared with 40). The flowrate of this flood had probably not been matched since the great flood of 1875, and a large acreage of agricultural land – filmed from the air by Northumbrian Water engineers – was under water. In the village of Brafferton north of Darlington, residents were evacuated from houses where noone could recall any previous inundation.

In Darlington, the river came out of its concrete channel on to the Ring Road and over the bridge at Priestgate (Plate 3.2), whilst Haughton Road was covered to a depth of four feet. However, property flooding there was very limited. The capacity of the many times enlarged flood channel was now sufficient to contain all but the very largest of floods.

However, engineering success has come at a price. The functional flume-like concrete channel can hardly be regarded as a civic amenity. The inhabitants of Darlington now must pay the price for the disregard which an earlier generation gave to the elements of physical geography by building on an active floodplain.

REFERENCES
1. Morden Carrs Drainage Board. Minutes.
2. Wear and Tees River Board. Annual Reports 1952 to 1965.

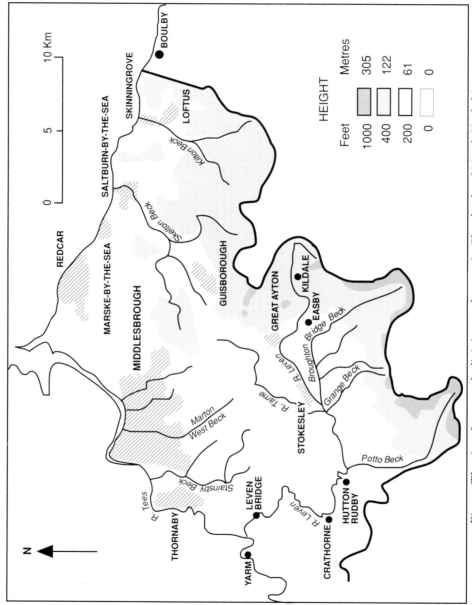

Fig 4.1 The river Leven and adjoining catchments in Cleveland and North Yorkshire.

4. THE RIVER LEVEN

*It is with rivers as it is with people; the greatest
are not always the most agreable nor the best to live with.*
Henry Van Dyke Little Rivers Chapter 2

The river Leven, a southern tributary of the Tees, drains the lowlands south of Middlesborough (Figure 4.1). It rises on the margin of the Cleveland Hills and is unusual as it is the only river in Northumbria which flows westward for the greater part of its course. In its lower reaches it turns northward and joins the Tees downstream from Yarm.

Along its east-west course from Great Ayton through Stokesley to Craythorne, it collects a series of parallel tributary streams flowing northward from the margins of the Cleveland Hills, the most easterly being the upper Leven itself and the most westerly the curiously named Potto beck. The watershed between these tributaries and the southward flowing tributaries of the river Rye lies close to the edge of the hills, so that the only substantial upland area in the Leven catchment lies in the headwaters of the main river, around Kildale.

The direction of the upper Leven above Kildale provides evidence that it previously flowed east into the Esk system but glaciation has diverted it at an acute angle from its original course. The Leven below Kildale, with the augmented flow from the captured stream, has cut a steep and deeply-incised gorge from which it emerges at Easby.

Topography, especially the orientation of the hill front, exerts a strong influence on storm rainfall patterns and creates quite different flood characteristics from other rivers of Northumbria. The worst flood conditions arise on the Leven when it is affected by a moist northerly or north-easterly airstream on the northern flank of a depression located over the sea off East Anglia. Orographic uplift over the Cleveland Hills can produce intense and sometimes prolonged rainfall when other rivers in Northumbria are hardly affected.

The town of Stokesley has been the principal sufferer from Leven floods but other riverside towns and villages have been affected, especially in earlier days when more rural industries lined the channel.

EARLY FLOOD RECORDS

There is a medieval record of flooding on the Leven which refers to the mill belonging to the Percy family who were lords of the manor at Kildale[1,2]. In 1321, 'the said mill was totally destroyed by a great inundation' and John, son of Arnald, was unable to rebuild it for two years owing to the heavy price he had paid as a ransom to the Scots.

There is no further information until the early eighteenth century and then only sketchy notes for neighbouring streams from the diary of Ralph Ward[3], a resident of Guisborough. He refers to two significant floods, one in June 1725 and the other at the end of October 1754 when prolonged rainfall

caused a very great flood. Seldom a bigar has been known in these parts. In my way to Boulby (on the coast near Staithes) went by Dale House Mill to view the bridge how it was after the great flood, all about it lookt well but that the flood there seemed not to have been so high by 3 or 4 feet as that of June 1725.

On the Leven itself the next recorded flood was at the beginning of October 1824[4]. The Rector of Stokesley, Archdeacon Vernon Harcourt, recorded in his diary how, after he had been entertaining a dumb visitor to the Rectory for some time,

he then took his leave but it was impossible for him to leave the house – the rains had swelled the becks with such an unusual flood that the house was completely insulated during our mute conversation and nothing but water was to be seen all around.

THE GREAT DAM-BREAK FLOOD OF 1840

There followed what was described decades later as the Great Flood of 1840[4]. It occurred in the early morning of 22 July 1840 after an extraordinarily intense summer storm. The flow in the Leven was augmented by the failure of two dams at Kildale, described in more detail in Chapter 10.

The dam-break wave rushed from the narrow defile at Easby and smashed against the weir, opposite Postgate's school in Ayton, which immediately gave way. The water rose five or six feet vertically in less than a minute, and swept down High Street where it reached above door-top level at a stable adjacent to Dr Loy's house, a large stone building which still exists. It carried away a cart-horse next to the blacksmith's shop, overtopped a stone bridge at Great Ayton and washed away its walls. Riverside industries suffered most, including two tanyards at High Green and one at Low Green. Both the oil mill and the corn mill lost their weirs. Many houses were flooded to a depth of four feet and some to as much as six feet. The flood happened during the night and the water rose so rapidly that there was little opportunity for rescuing household goods. Remarkably, no life was lost on the Leven, although a man was surrounded and drowned at Lealholm bridge on the neighbouring river Esk. This illustrates the magnitude of the storm even without the added effects of dam failures.

In Great Ayton the water was five or six feet higher than had previously been observed. Little information is available from Stokesley: though it was deeply flooded, it was said to be only one foot deeper than had been known before – probably in 1824.

Stokesley figures frequently in the accounts of subsequent floods but Great Ayton is mentioned rarely. Flooding at Stokesley was reported on 29 September 1852 and again on Thursday 30 August 1866[5], the day of the annual agricultural show. The showground and access roads were so flooded that it had to be postponed, surprisingly only until the next day. Meanwhile in the town, the streets were knee deep and a large number of riverside houses was flooded to a similar depth.

As on many other Northumbrian rivers, flooding was unusually frequent and severe during the period from 1875 to 1903. The flood of 14 November 1875 was the biggest since 1840 and most of Stokesley High Street was under water. The parish church was undergoing repairs at the time and morning services were being held in the town hall. The service was brought to a hasty conclusion as the waters began to lap through the doorway and the parishioners had to make their escape through the rising waters[5]. Several of the town's wooden bridges were carried away and Wiggins and Sons' brewhouse, adjoining the river, had its large doors washed open and barrels swept away. Many other small becks, from Teesside to the Cleveland Hills, overflowed and caused damage. At the village of Hutton Lowcross near Guisborough the beck hit the end wall of a row of cottages with such force that it collapsed. The dividing walls also gave way, making the five cottages into a single, tangled room. At Middlesborough the combined effects of high tide and rainfall brought flooding along the Ormesby beck. This was the first of a long sequence of flooding incidents in the town.

There was flooding again, mainly of agricultural land, along the Leven on 21 December the following year. An unusual combination of thunderstorms, snowmelt and gale force winds produced further flooding on 15 November 1878. At Stokesley, communication between the town and the railway station was cut off. The street was covered to three feet deep in places and houses to nearly two feet. The workhouse boys took advantage of the occasion and were seen sailing in a tin bath around their yard. At Hutton Rudby a sail factory was seriously damaged.

Two years later on 28 October 1880 there was again heavy rain with an easterly gale which exacted a heavy toll along the north–east coast where dozens of vessels were wrecked. At Stokesley the water was two feet deep; the gas mains were flooded and the town was left in darkness. There were two deaths in incidents in 1889 and 1892. The postmaster of Great Ayton lost his life in a flood in 1889 of unknown date and on 15 October 1892 a boy was drowned when washed off a footbridge.

FLOODS OF THE TWENTIETH CENTURY

The flood of 9 October 1903 was undoubtedly the highest since 1875 and was also the first of a long sequence of well-documented events that affected Stokesley during the present century. The town hall which stands in the middle of the market square is one of the first buildings to be affected, and a careful record of levels in the building has been maintained there. These enable us to compare flood magnitudes (Table 4.1).

Although the record shows that the 1903 flood was the second biggest since 1900, there were few reports of effects on the Leven, mainly because there was competing news on a horrifying scale from all round the Northumbrian region. The *Darlington and Stockton Times* merely reported that the auction mart, the police station and many homes were flooded in Stokesley and that the village of Leven Bridge was flooded and the road impassable. In neighbouring parts of Cleveland the Marton beck flooded hundreds of houses in North Ormesby. At

Saltburn a stone bridge, built only a couple of years previously over the Skelton beck, was totally demolished.

The wartime floods of 1914 and 1915 were again little noted and that of 1928 barely reached the lower houses in Stokesley though it did enormous damage in Middlesborough and adjoining areas when Marton and Ormesby becks again overflowed.

Table 4.1
Flood dates and levels at Stokesley town hall since 1900.

Date	Level at town hall (metres above floor level)	Level at town hall (metres above Ordnance Datum)	Remarks
9 Oct. 1903	0.76	67.24	
16 July 1914	Not known		Daily rainfall 80.5 mm at Kildale
23 July 1915	Not known		
14 June 1928	Not known		Levenside cut off from rest of town.
22 July 1930	1.00	67.47	Highest this century.
5 Sep. 1931	0.62	67.10	
17 July 1940	0.26	66.72	
24 Aug. 1954	0.33	67.78	
10 Oct. 1960	0.26	66.72	
6 Mar. 1963	–		Lapping into Levenside
5 Nov. 1967	0.13	66.60	
3 Nov. 1968	0.50	66.96	
11 Sep. 1976	0.70	67.18	

'GOD HELP THEM WHEN THE TIDE COMES IN' – 1930
The great flood of 23 July 1930, the largest of the century, could hardly be overlooked. Apart from its severity it was much more localised in Cleveland and North Yorkshire.

The early summer of 1930 had been warm and dry but the weather broke on St Swithin's Day (15 July), with sufficient rainfall over the next five days to wet the catchment in advance of the deluges from 20 to 23 July. An astonishing total of over 250 mm of rain fell at Kildale Hall in the headwaters of the Leven and also at the nearby Lockwood reservoir. This was more than a quarter of the normal year's total. Rainfall was generally over 50 mm on the 20th and several stations recorded over 100 mm on the 22nd. As in many floods on the Leven the rain was accompanied by a driving north-east wind.

The flood began in Stokesley on the afternoon of Tuesday 22, first on the approach roads from Middlesborough and at the station, and it then crept into the town. Houses in Levenside were flooded, and houses and shops on the south side of the High Street were affected. In the market square, the water had already surrounded the police station but Inspector Nelson, who had recently arrived in the town, was blissfully unaware that his sitting room was already under six inches of water; he had gone away on leave earlier in the day.

The rain eased off in the evening and residents walked out to view the swirling waters. Late in the evening the water showed signs of receding, and newcomers to the town went trustfully to bed whilst those with a longer memory kept getting up to monitor the level. After a renewed burst of rainfall, the river suddenly rose again early on Wednesday morning and by daybreak nearly the whole town was awash (Fig 4.2). Stokesley was virtually isolated from the outside world, all the access roads being flooded, and deprived of basic services. Electricity and telephone communications were cut; the gas works were flooded, cooking was impossible as both stoves and fuel were under water. Dry food was hard to find. Marion Hall graphically catalogues the course of the flood through the streets and buildings of the town[6].

The water was washing over the counter in Mr West's chemist's shop. Mr Holden a new grocer close to, had most of his stock ruined. The water was three feet deep in the Police Station and breast high for a man outside. Young Howie of the Beckside waded breast deep to set his pigeons free. Pollard's house near Silver Street was 5 feet deep. Mrs Collings on West Green 3 feet deep. Mrs Auton's up to the second stair (in a raised house): 4 steps high in Mrs Grange's at the Back Lane West End. 18 inches high in Miss Auton's near Providence Yard. About a foot in D. W. Richardson's on the south ridge of High Street and Mrs Kearsley's. In Commercial Row 4 or 5 feet deep in F. Hugill's house; 3 feet in Mr Warren's 1 foot in Mr Peacock's, dry in old Mr Armstrong's; foot or so in Butcher Scotts; poured through Farrow and Kitching's draper's shop who saved much material: but the floor very wet: the Wesley Methodist chapel dry. The water over Mr Morton's sewing machine.

Higher houses in College Square near Church House and the Primitive Methodist chapel escaped but the floodwaters extended up Springfield past the New Inn. Nearby, a Redwing bus lay partly submerged and passengers had to be rescued by ferry. A short reach of the road stood above water level but further along, at the workhouse, tramps staying in 'the casual ward' were awakened by the sound of water lapping under their wooden beds.

The younger people of the town took the flood in their stride. Many had spent Tuesday checking on their neighbours and moving furniture to upper floors. Photographers had a field day and scenes of flooded Stokesley appeared on postcards for several years afterwards (Plate 4.1). Soup kitchens were set up in dry houses in Handyside and deliveries were made by horse and wagon to beleaguered residents.

A young manager from Dorman Long's, living in Stokesley, managed to wade to nearby Maltby to telephone to his works with the message 'Send a boat

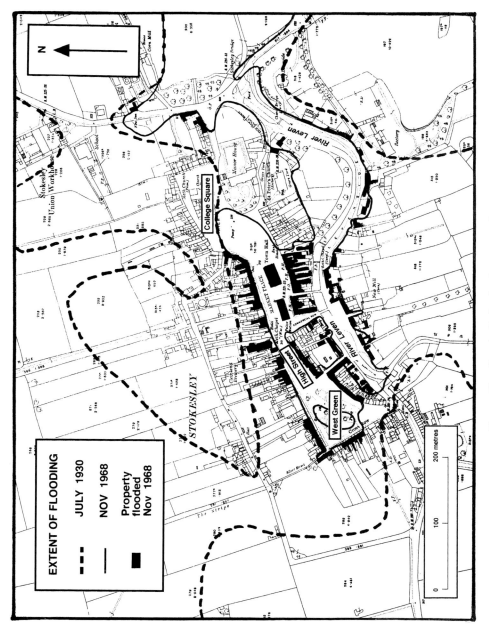

Fig 4.2 Flooding in Stokesley in 1930 and 1968.

Plate 4.1 West Green, Stokesley during the flood of 23 July 1930.

complete with sailor'. In due course a coble arrived on the back of a lorry and the sailor, a Swede and unfamiliar with the local geography, was heard to exclaim on arrival, 'This is terrible but God help them when the tide comes in!'. The boat was soon in action carrying food and ferrying the more deeply submerged residents to dry land.

The waters began to recede at eleven o'clock on Wednesday morning and traffic began to move slowly again, bringing relief but also hordes of unwanted, gaping sightseers. During the afternoon the task of clearing up began: pumping, bailing, sweeping and hanging out of sodden floor coverings. Electricity and gas were only restored by Friday. A belated consequence of the flood was the outbreak of disease in September and there were fatalities from typhoid, diptheria and scarlet fever.

Many other villages and large tracts of agricultural land were affected all along the Leven. At Great Ayton, the river came on to the High Street, and Squire bridge was washed away. Downstream, at Leven Bridge, only the top of the hump-back was visible and residents watched from bedroom windows as tree trunks, sheep and chests-of-drawers swept on their journey to the Tees.

There was not long to wait till flood waters struck again in the late summer of 1931. Rainfall on the hills was very similar to the previous year with over 100mm in one day. However, in the adjacent lowlands 59mm fell at Albert Park, Middlesborough, on 4 September, far exceeding the daily total of 31mm in July the previous year. Although the level on the Leven at Stokesley fell some distance short of that in the previous year, the conditions at Middlesborough were far worse[7]. There, over two miles of streets were flooded and 511 houses affected. Water was up to the window sills in North Ormesby Road and at Cargo Fleet. Just across the Tees there was serious concern when the Saltworks dam failed at Haverton Hill (Chapter 10).

Work had begun the previous November on a flood relief scheme in Middlesborough, but was insufficiently advanced to improve the situation. Indeed, there were grounds for belief that the works in progress impeded the flow in Marton beck, whose swollen waters were the chief source of the flooding. There were demands for the sacking of the borough engineer, and calls for full compensation for the householders were strenuously supported by the M.P., Miss Ellen Wilkinson, and the executive committee of the Middlesborough Unemployed Association.

With the memories of the previous year still fresh in their minds the residents along the Leven made an early start to their precautions, but though many houses were again flooded in Stokesley the flood was neither as severe nor as prolonged as in the previous year. At Great Ayton the mill race overflowed into Bridge Street, affecting many homes including Captain Cook's old house which was unoccupied at the time. Water poured against the rear of the premises through the house and spurted under the front door. Nearby, at Station Road corner, children from the infant's school were carried through the floods by Mr Robinson, a council workman.

Nearly ten years passed before the next flood on 17 July 1940. This was by no means as serious but still affected a number of houses in Levenside. Reporting of the flooding was prohibited as of other wartime events and the only information available is the recorded level at the town hall and the daily rainfall record of 87.1mm in one day at Kildale.

'THE FAIR WEATHER WILL CONTINUE'
The flood of August 1954 came at the end of a damp and unpleasant summer in north-east England. The Wear and Tees River Board in their annual report remarked that a notable feature of the rainfall was its persistence and continuity during the summer and autumn months and that, because of the soaked nature of the catchment areas, the rivers responded rapidly to rainfall[8].

A BBC weather forecast on 19 August that 'the fair weather will continue' surely justifies inclusion in Stephen Pile's *Book of Heroic Failures*[9]. Elsewhere in the region it drew angry comments from farmers both for its inaccurate description of immediate past weather and unjustified optimism for the future. In Sunderland, 19 August was the coldest August day for nine years. In the Upper Leven catchment 105 mm of rain had fallen between 15 and 19 August; a further 33 mm fell on the 20th and 51 mm on the 23rd.

The flood rose over bank level on 21 August and riverside houses in Stokesley had their floors covered with a shallow layer of mud-laden water. In the continuing rain residents did not have the opportunity to dry out their carpets and furniture before the river rose again in the early hours of 24 August. The high street resembled a miniature lake. The police station was surrounded (Plate

Plate 4.2 A police officer ventures out from his flooded station in Stokesley on 24 August 1954. *Photo.* Evening Gazette.

4.2) and the downstairs offices and unoccupied cells were under two feet of water. The *Northern Echo* reported:

As the milkman went his rounds, his sturdy cob trotted through the water which reached his belly-band. The postwoman was not deterred, though her home was one of the worst affected in Levenside. She trudged through the floods to reach the Post Office or carried on with her duties as best she could.

FIRST PLANS FOR THE RELIEF OF STOKESLEY

A further flood, with similar consequences, occurred on 10 October 1960. By this time residents of Stokesley were thoroughly sick of the repeated loss and inconvenience. However, works to protect Stokesley posed a particular problem. The river is a most attractive feature of the town in normal flows. The conventional solutions of widening, deepening, streamlining and embanking would have done irreparable damage, and the residents had never been in favour of these solutions. In the wake of the 1930 flood, the opinion had been expressed that the widening and straightening of the tortuous course downstream from Stokesley would be sufficient to reduce the water levels through the town. This view was expressed after every flood.

In 1961 the Board prepared a scheme to relieve flooding in Stokesley at a cost of £169,000[10]. Although it included improvements to the Leven downstream of Stokesley, hydraulic analysis showed that, whilst this measure might help, it would be inadequate in itself to solve the problem. This view was confirmed

59

by the events of 1976. The main proposal was for the construction of a diversion channel one kilometre in length, to carry the floodwaters of the Leven around Stokesley and into the Eller beck (Fig 4.3). The enlargement of the Eller beck was proposed to convey the combined flows from the junction of the bypass channel near Broughton bridge to the junction with the Leven below Stokesley at Bense bridge.

The scheme was submitted to the Ministry of Agriculture Fisheries and Food in February 1963 and was rejected on the grounds that the value of the likely benefits was substantially less than the likely cost of the scheme.

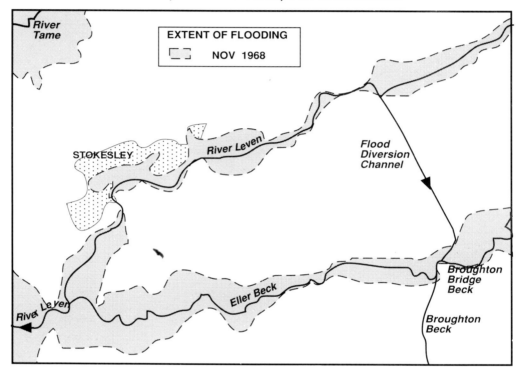

Fig 4.3 The diversion of the river Leven into the Broughton Bridge beck, completed in 1978 to alleviate flooding in Stokesley.

LEVEN STRIKES BACK

Within a month of the decision the Leven again showed that it was not to be ignored. It crept onto riverside pathways and threatened riverside houses on 6 March 1963. The event was unusual in that it was the only one in the record caused solely by the thawing of snow. In this way the Leven differs from larger catchments originating in the Pennines where snowmelt floods are common.

Flooding returned in November 1967 and again on 3 November 1968, bringing the worst conditions since 1931. Over 100 mm of rain fell at a steady rate over a three-day period on a catchment already saturated from autumn rainfall. For the first time BBC cameras recorded the swirling waters through the market place. Over 160 properties were flooded, some of them by the wash from passing vehicles (Fig 4.2).

Of course these floods gave impetus to the reconsideration of flood alleviation and a scheme was again proposed by Northumbrian River Authority which differed little from the earlier scheme but now cost £204,000[11]. It was approved by the Ministry in July 1971[12].

However, local landowners opposed the scheme, insisting that, whilst it would relieve Stokesley, it would also exacerbate flooding on their land downstream. Land negotiations were protracted and there were further delays due to the reorganisation of the water industry and local government which now seemed unsure of the practicalities of the scheme. The Northumbrian Water Authority, which was formed in 1974, attempted to allay these fears by carrying out preliminary works to increase channel capacities through agricultural land downstream from Stokesley.

Work finally began in October 1975 and was programmed to take two-and-a-half years to complete. It progressed steadily through the long dry summer of 1976, with works concentrated on channel enlargement on the Leven below Stokesley and on the Eller beck. However, when Leven had its final fling on 12 September 1976, the new diversion channel was not yet available to carry the flow around Stokesley[13,14].

On that day, in common with most of England, the north-east – and especially the Cleveland Hills – suffered an extraordinary rainfall whilst water authorities and the Government were finalising their emergency plans for the drought. In the upper reaches of the Leven, 200 mm rainfall fell in forty hours (Fig 4.4). It was fortunate for Stokesley that the rain fell on exceptionally dry soil which retained a large proportion of the rainfall. Less than thirty percent of the rainfall contributed to flood runoff compared with seventy percent for the 1968 storm.

Nevertheless, the flooding was again serious. Twelve houses in Great Ayton were penetrated. Flooding commenced in Stokesley on Saturday evening and by 7 a.m. on Sunday when the river reached its peak, the level was six inches higher than in 1968 (Plate 4.3). About 150 properties were affected, fewer than in 1968 because there was less vehicle wash from the Sunday traffic. Six elderly people were rescued from their houses by policemen in diving gear[5]. The travelling fair, with stalls on the cobbled market place, was hastily removed to higher parts of the town.

The works for the flood alleviation scheme also suffered damage from erosion where new banks had not had time to stabilise and grow protection. A new pumping chamber was a total loss. At Kirby bridge part of an abutment collapsed, and Broughton bridge also suffered damage. Remedial works were delayed in the continuing wet weather through the autumn. However, they were finally completed on schedule with a final estimated cost of £525,000 in March 1978.

And so the Leven has finally been tamed – or has it? Flooding of agricultural land on the flood plain still continues regularly, mainly in the Tame tributary

61

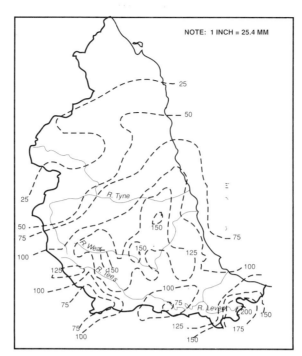

NOTE: 1 INCH = 25.4 MM

Fig 4.4 Rainfall over Northumbria on 11-12 September 1976 with greatest amounts in the headwaters of the river Leven.

Plate 4.3 The river Leven overflows into Levenside 12 September 1976.

62

and in the Leven downstream from Stokesley. The level of protection in these areas has been recently reviewed and works have been carried out on the Tame to diminish the frequency of flooding. A few houses in Great Ayton remain vulnerable.

However, Stokesley has clearly benefited from the scheme. It would certainly have flooded in an isolated but intense rainstorm on 26 August 1987 had it not been for the diversion channel. But, like all flood protection schemes, this alleviates but does not prevent flooding. The Stokesley scheme is designed to protect against the occurrence of a rare flood, in this case one that can be expected to recur on average once in forty years. But an even larger and rarer flood can be expected eventually, like the flood of 1930, or a combination of the initial wet ground conditions of the 1968 flood with the rainfall of September 1976. In such circumstances there would still be a few wet feet in Stokesley though the extent and depth of the flood would be very much less. Let us hope that such a flood will be long delayed.

REFERENCES
 1. Guisboro Chatulary, Surtees Society, no 86
 2. Page, W. (ed.) *The Victoria History of the Counties of England. A History of Yorkshire, North Riding*, vol. 2, (London, 1923)
 3. Whiting. C. E. (ed.) *Two Yorkshire Diaries: The Diary of Arthur Jessop and Ralph Ward's Journal*, (Yorkshire Archaeological Society Record Series, no 117, 1952)
 4. Blakeborough, J. F. *Bits of West Cleveland, Great Ayton, Stokesley and District, Past and Present*, (Middlesborough, 1901)
 5. Boyes, M. 'Floodtime at Stokesley', *The Dalesman*, no 1, 39, (1977)
 6. Hall M. 'The Flood at Stokesley, July 1930', in Wright, A. and Mawes, J. (eds) *Stokesley Selection*, (Great Ayton, 1982)
 7. Lillie, W. *The History of Middlesborough, An Illustration of the Evolution of English Industry*, (Middlesborough Corporation, 1968)
 8. Wear and Tees River Board. Fifth Annual Report 1955
 9. Pile, S. *The Book of Heroic Failures*, (London, 1979)
10. Wear and Tees River Board 'Stokesley Flood Relief Scheme', Chief Engineer's Report, (1961)
11. Northumbrian River Authority 'Stokesley Flood Relief Scheme', Engineer's Report, (1969)
12. Watson, R. M. 'Stokesley Flood Relief Scheme'. Paper presented to Inst. Water Engineers and Scientists, (March 1979)
13. Northumbrian Water Authority 'Flooding on 11/12 September 1976'. Unpublished Internal Report, Tees Division, (1976)
14. Northumbrian Water Authority 'Flooding on the River Leven on 11/12 September 1976 and its Historical Significance'. Unpublished Internal Report, Research and Data Collection Section, (1976)

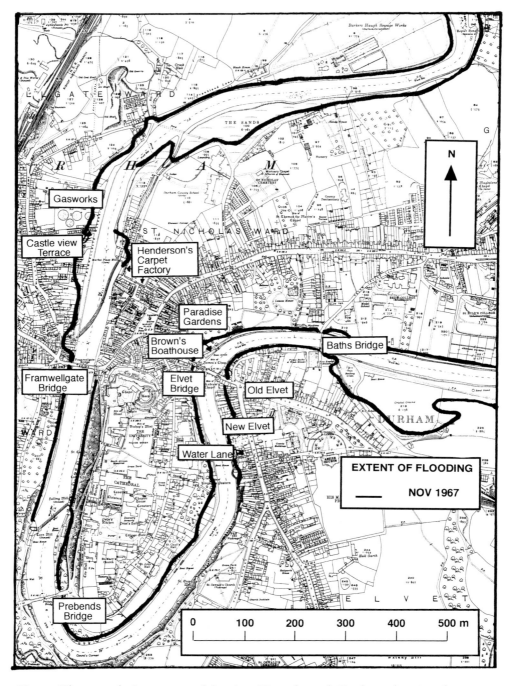

Fig 5.1 The meandering course of the river Wear through Durham showing the extent of the flood of November 1967 and locations noted in the text.

5. THE RIVER WEAR

The floods are risen O Lord, the floods lift up
their voices; the floods lift up their waves.
The Lord on high is mightier than the noise of many waters

Psalm 93,3

There is no more magnificent sight in the whole of England than the view that awaits the traveller approaching Durham City by train. There, across the narrow valley of the river Wear, stands Durham Cathedral, a monument to the glory of God, the veneration of St Cuthbert and the creative skill of its Norman architects. It is perched on top of its steeply wooded hill, dominated by its mighty central tower and flanked to the north by the Bishop's castle.

But without the river Wear Durham would not exist. It is the creator and sustainer of the city, with its encircling and protecting meander which supplied water to its early inhabitants and released power for its medieval mills. The river also provides a setting which has drawn artist, poet and tourist. The Wear in all its moods and colours, its medieval bridges and weirs, provides the foreground and reflection for the city's ancient stones.

The concord between river and city has sometimes been shaken when the river has risen and torn at the very fabric of bridges and dwellings. The steep banks on the Wear's horseshoe loop around Durham permit only a narrow footpath alongside but, at the upper and lower ends of the loop, the valley widens out to allow room for settlements at Elvet and Framwellgate (Fig. 5.1). It is here that flood waters, both ancient and modern, have spread out for the distress of the inhabitants. Although other places along the river Wear have suffered inundation, Durham City has most often been the focus of attention.

However, the source of the floods of Durham, almost without exception, has been on the Pennine moors, where the river rises forty kilometres to the west, and the high half circle of hills from Bollihope Common and Ireshope Moor, through Burnhope Seat to Killhope Law, seem to hem the valley in from the influences of the neighbouring Tees and South Tyne (Fig. 5.2). This is the land of the 'hopes', the steep hidden valleys rising in haggy and mossy moorland and tumbling in gravel beds to the main valley below (Plate 5.1). 'Hope' was an old Saxon name for enclosed valley, and its use with 'burn' for the stream distinguishes the Wear from the adjacent Tees and Tyne where such streams are often 'becks' and 'gills', a witness to the Viking influence which spread up from the south but passed Weardale by.

The upper Wear is also sheltered from the full strength of the rain-laden westerly winds which sweep across the Eden valley and spend their greatest force on the western face of Cross Fell. Nevertheless, the Wear watershed has

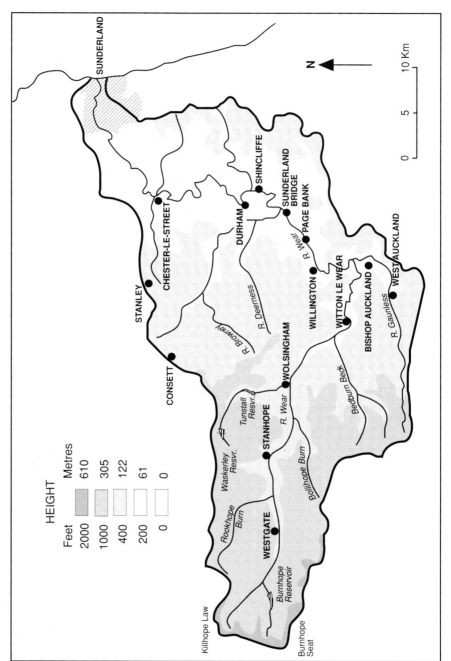

Fig 5.2 The river Wear and its catchment

Plate 5.1 From the moorland of Burnhope Seat, where cottongrass and cloudberry are reflected in boggy pools, there is a view towards Burnhope reservoir and down the Wear Valley to Westgate. *Photo. D. Archer*

Plate 5.2 Prebend's bridge, Durham, built after its predecessor was washed away in the flood of 17 November 1771. Taken from the position of the south abutment of the earlier bridge. Through the arch is the former corn mill, rebuilt after destruction in 1771. *Photo. D. Archer*

still enough height to catch a blast of these winds on its damp and impermeable peat. Annual rainfall of 1800 mm on Burnhope Seat is perhaps only 400 mm lower than on the Cross Fell ridge (Fig. 1.2). As on neighbouring catchments little of the rain is absorbed and it quickly finds its way into the channel network.

The upper Wear takes its name below the Burnhope confluence at the village of Wearhead. The upper valley bears the evidence of the retreat of the ice at the end of the last Ice Age with thick deposits of coarse gravels and sands laid down as the summer meltwater from the dying ice sheet poured down the valley. The post-glacial river has incised itself in these gravels and left a sequence of terrace features[1]. Villages and roads lie on these terraces which are generally well beyond the reach of modern floods. Adjacent valley sides also fall in steps where horizontal beds of hard limestone form bluffs of grey rock, which are often accentuated by quarrying. Whin Sill rocks cut across the valley floor at Cowshill and above Stanhope where the river has created a narrow gorge. The river flows nearly due east and is joined by the Rookhope and Stanhope burns and Waskerley beck from the north and the Bollihope burn and the forested Bedburn beck from the south.

The valley floor widens out at Witton-le-Wear and the river begins to meander on an active floodplain. At Bishop Auckland the Wear is joined by the river Gaunless and as it approaches the scarp of the Magnesian limestone it turns sharply towards the north-east and assumes the orientation of the scarp. The river often overtops its banks on its course to Durham and, although there are few buildings within reach of the river, the bridges have occasionally succumbed.

Like other valleys of Northumbria, the Wear has a buried channel, cut in solid rock far below the present bed, and created at some remote and uncertain era when the sea level was much lower, perhaps by forty metres, than at present. During the last glaciation the buried valley was choked with deposits and, in attempting to re-establish its course after the disappearance of the ice, the river found its original course blocked at several points. The classic example is at Durham City where the river imprinted its new meandering course on solid rock. Another much longer gorge section of the Wear extends from just north of Durham to Lumley, where the present river has incised its course to the east of the buried valley.

At Chester-le-Street an even more remarkable diversion occurred. The pre-glacial Wear continued northward along the valley of what is now the Team to join the river Tyne near Newcastle. Blockage of that route caused the Wear to turn sharp eastward where it has cut its present gorge-like lower course through the hard rock of the Magnesian limestone outcrop, to join the sea at Sunderland. The tide extends inland along this reach a distance of sixteen kilometres to Lambton bridge.

These glacial diversions have a significant bearing on vulnerability to flooding. The narrow incision of their gorge-like sections has discouraged extensive development adjacent to the river and, with the exception of Durham City, few settlements have been at risk on the main channel. The main flooding on tributary streams has been on the river Gaunless at South Church, the river Browney at Lanchester, and the Cong burn at Chester-le-Street.

Although the Wear has only a marginally lower gradient than its neighbours the Tees and Tyne, it does not have the same historic reputation for generating flash floods with a steep wave front. Nevertheless, it is the Wear which has recorded in recent years the most dramatic event of this kind.

THE EARLY RECORD
Information on ancient floods is tantalisingly brief but the survival of some records suggests that these were events of some note. The first flood on record was that which occurred on St Swithin's Day 15 July 1316[2]. This summer flood resulted in 'bursting dams, breaking down mills, and rushing into houses drowning men women and children'. In 1401 it is reported that Framwellgate Bridge was rebuilt after destruction by flood[3].

There are no accounts from the sixteenth century but four short reports from the seventeenth. The first of these, in the *Gentleman's Magazine*, records a great storm of wind and rain on 1 August 1648 which caused two of the best collieries on the river Wear to be drowned. Then a series of records in the 1680s documents an exceptionally wet decade. A wet spring followed the flood on the Tees in January 1682. 'It began to rain on 10 April and so continued.' On the night of the 25th 'it rained very much that waters came out...that people hardly could stirre abroad' and 'there was a great flood on the river Wear at Durham on 26 and 27 April'.

Jacob Bee's diary[4] provides the first hint of flooding at Elvet in Durham the following year on 3 August 1683.

On August 3rd, the Assizes began at Durham and such an inundation of water yt ye Judges were forcet to come down Gillygate and came in at about 8 at night and read their commission.

They were probably delayed because the flood blocked the approach to Elvet bridge. Bee's diary records three further floods in Durham in 1689 'about St Luke's Day (18 October) which exceeded all the floods that had been there for many years'. This coincides with a very early record of severe flooding on the river Ouse at York.

There was then a gap of thirty-three years before the next event, Slater's flood, was reported: this is unusual in being named after a dead man. Slater had been one of the bailiffs of Durham and his body was being brought from St Nicholas Church on 8 July for burial at St Oswald's. The parish register of St Oswald's recalls:

Ye river was risen so high yt they could not bring the corps up New Elvet but were obliged to carry it up Old Elvet and Ratten Row. It was ye greatest flood yt had been in ye memory of man.

In the same flood the bridge over the Wear at Wolsingham was broken down and the county considered it necessary 'to build a footbridge until a bridge of stone for carts and carriages may be built[5]'.

Two June floods of 1727 severed communication between Durham and Shincliffe, but neither was said to reach the height of Slater's flood. Shincliffe was even more severely affected in the flood of 17 February 1753 when its medieval bridge was overturned[6]. The flood 'broke down two arches and prostrated the pillar between the two arches nearest to Durham, entire into the river without breaking[7]'. The bridge on the site had had a chequered history: first built in 1368, when the Durham Account Rolls record the spending of eleven shillings and four pence towards its construction, it was rebuilt with two arches in 1400 by Bishop Skirlaw and again around 1540 'after being throwne downe for lake of Reparations in tyme' (Leland[8]).

The flood of 1753 followed a thaw and, unusually for such an event, 'the river rose so suddenly that most of the houses [presumably in Durham] which stood on its banks were filled to the upper stories before the inhabitants had time to quit them'.

Another medieval bridge, that at Sunderland Bridge, Croxdale, which carried the Great North Road, was repeatedly in the news the following decade. The bridge had been built before 1346 when it received its first mention in an account of a skirmish with the Scots under Douglas. It had been repaired after the flood of 1722 and again in 1750 when it was reported that the abutments were being undermined[5]. The first direct account of flooding in the area was on 9 November 1760 when the mail coach was held up at the bridge and the London mail had to be transferred to horseback[9].

The south arch of the bridge fell down in May 1769, although there is no indication that this happened during a flood. The northern arch was also reported to be in bad condition and both were rebuilt in their present form a few months later. The strengthening was probably instrumental in preserving the structure in the great flood of 1771. But even before that, on 8 November 1770, 'the river rose the height of three stories in [into?] the house of Mr Mitchell innkeeper adjacent to the bridge'. The flood was severe enough to cover the lower parts of Elvet and a boat plied for some time along the road.

THE GREAT FLOOD OF 1771 ON THE WEAR

The flood of 17 November 1771 on the Wear as on the Tyne and the Tees was by far the greatest in the historic period[9,10,11]. At Durham it was reported to be eight feet ten inches higher than had ever been known (probably in comparison to the flood of 1753), and at Sunderland seven feet higher. Bridges at Frosterley, Wolsingham and Witton-le-Wear were destroyed.

In Durham, the stone bridge built in 1696, belonging to the dean and chapter and standing just upstream from the site of the present Prebend's bridge, was swept away except for the abutments. The solidly-built medieval Elvet or New bridge, which had remained intact since it was built around 1180, had four arches breached. The openings were completely filled and the bridge face could not withstand the full force of the torrent. The waters swept through Old and New Elvet at the east end. Two houses were destroyed and 'all the inhabitants in the lower part of the two Elvets sustained great damage'.

Across the loop, Framwellgate bridge with its higher arches survived, but two houses at the end of the bridge were swept away, with their contents. One of the Abbey Mills on the side of South Street was destroyed.

Remarkably, no lives were lost in Durham, but downstream two servants at Cocken House were drowned in attempting to cross at Cockenford. Nearby a mill and mill houses were carried away. The river banks between Cocken and Chester-le-Street were strewn with the carcasses of horses, cattle and sheep. At Lumley a boathouse and fishing lodge were destroyed and the fishery dam was swept away[12]. At Chester-le-Street the water backed up the Cong burn into the town and extended two hundred yards north to south in the street. In the tidal reach the river broke in and filled the collieries at North Biddick, Chattershaugh and Low Lambton and thirty-four pit ponies were drowned.

The flood wave reached Sunderland at two o'clock on Sunday morning. Many river bank inhabitants at the staithes were saved by breaking through their roofs and by being taken off by boat. One staith was completely carried away.

However, at the river mouth the alarming velocity was a greater problem than the rise in level. Most of the ships in the harbour were torn adrift and jostled helplessly in the current. Cracking hulls and the roar of the river mingled with the desperate cries for help by the boys left on board (most men being on shore). But little help could be given. Morning revealed thirty-four ships wrecked on the bar and north and south sand. Keels were still being driven to sea by the dozen and continued most of the day. An estimated three hundred of the seven hundred keels on the Wear were set adrift and a good number were destroyed. *The Journal* reported that many men and boys were lost but did not specify the number.

A frantic search for flooded property started immediately on banks and coast. Looters were discouraged with stern penalties. The work of the port of Sunderland remained depressed for some months because of the temporary loss of the coal pits and the depletion of shipping.

At Durham, Prebend's bridge was started in 1772 to replace its ruined predecessor (Plate 5.2). It took six years to complete. The arches of Elvet bridge were rebuilt in essentially their original form.

A QUIET HALF CENTURY
Although the floods of the next half century were locally serious, none remotely matched 1771 or those that followed in the 1820s. A summary of these will suffice:

1777	26 Oct.	Intense local storm in upper Weardale.
1783	17 Nov.	Delays in mail due to flooding round Sunderland Bridge.
1787	10 Oct.	Bridge at Witton-le-Wear swept away.
1789	20 July	Rainfall concentrated in lower reaches. Flooding at Sunderland Bridge delayed passage. Much agricultural loss. Two mills, a skin mill and an iron forge mill, destroyed at Bracken hill on the Lumley Park burn. Houses flooded in Chester-le-Street. Said to be highest since 1771.
1792	26 Aug.	Said to be 'much damage done on the Wear'.

1815 30 Dec.   Agricultural losses on floodplain but more severe damage in Durham and Sunderland and to shipping from the associated hurricane. Paper mill dam at Moorsley Banks carried away.

WINTER SUMMER, AUTUMN – FLOODS OF THE 1820s

After an era of comparative quiescence the Wear struck three times in quick succession and in different seasons in 1822, 1824 and 1828.

The first occasion on 2 February 1822 caused significant problems for riverside dwellers, especially in the middle reaches. At Stanhope, where haugh lands were covered, the occupants of Unthank corn mill had to leave for safety. Butts House was inundated and could not be approached without wading through water four feet deep. Field walls were thrown down and fields were covered with sand and stones.

The river reached its peak at 5 a.m. at Durham and by then had spread out over the fields around Shincliffe and the racecourse (now the University playing fields), and into Paradise Gardens (now regrettably the coach park behind Elvet boathouse). During the night a small drama had developed at the east end of the racecourse. Mark Hopper, a farmer living in Elvet, began to feel anxious for his cattle as he watched the river rise. He went out with his son just before midnight to remove them to safety. However, Hopper and son were overtaken by rising water and only just managed to reach a haystack in the highest part of the field. They tethered the cows to the surrounding railing and hastily climbed the stack with a calf. There they remained until rescued by boat in the morning.

Two public houses in Elvet were awash. At Framwellgate Waterside, water spilled over the banks and entirely covered adjacent garden walls. There was still only limited building on the west bank but, on the opposite side, Henderson's woollen factory and the adjacent Back Lane suffered some damage.

Like its immediate predecessor, the flood of 10 to 11 October 1824 was accompanied by strong winds, described by the *Durham Advertiser* as a 'perfect hurricane'. Seventy to eighty vessels were wrecked off the north-east coast. The papers agreed that the river was at its highest at Durham since 1771. Houses in New Elvet and the Back Lane, amongst others, were flooded. 'All low grounds, cellars, kitchens of houses near the river were under water', and furniture was hurriedly removed during the night to higher floors. Fires in the retorts at the new gasworks at Framwellgate were extinguished. There was also serious damage on lowland tributaries including the Gaunless at West Auckland and the Browney, where a paper mill was flooded and several wooden bridges washed away.

Although the flood of 13 July 1828 was marginally lower than in 1824, agricultural losses were far greater because of the season. Corn fields were flattened and hay washed away or destroyed by being mixed with sand and gravel. At Houghall a flood bank recently constructed by Lord Viscount Barrington was washed away and riverside fields from Houghall to Durham were inundated. In the City the gasworks retorts were again covered and apology was made in the theatre for 'the darkness of the lights'.

Further downstream in the Lambton area, one tenant farmer, Mrs Gallon, 'a widow of great respectability' of Low Crook Farm, lost her entire produce from sixty acres. The *Durham Advertiser* took up the case of rent rebate.

This is a case of peculiar hardship but we have little doubt that from the humane character of Lord Durham to whom Mrs Gallon is tenant that the loss she has sustained will be taken into account at the next rent day.

At Sunderland a ship was carried away at Hetton staith and keels were driven from their moorings out to sea.

TROUBLE AT THE MILL

Amongst the buildings which suffered in the more severe floods of the nineteenth century was the Market Place mill, driven by water directed to its wheel by the ancient Framwellgate weir, which lay diagonally across the river. Alongside the mill, and presumably downstream from the weir, was a level gauge. Levels from this gauge were often given in Durham newspapers at the time of the flood but a comprehensive list from 1852 (Table 5.1) was provided by the *Durham Advertiser* following the October floods of 1903, thus enabling comparisons of flood severity to be made.

Table 5.1 Observed flood levels at Market Place mill, Durham.
(*Durham Advertiser* October 1903).

Date		Level
29 September	1852	14 feet 0 inches
16 June	1855	10 feet 0 inches
28 September	1856	11 feet 0 inches
6 March	1862	9 feet 2 inches
11 February	1868	9 feet 6 inches
14 November	1875	13 feet 0 inches
3 December	1876	10 feet 0 inches
13 November	1878	10 feet 9 inches
10 March	1881	11 feet 6 inches
6 November	1886	12 feet 6 inches
8 October	1892	10 feet 0 inches
9 October	1903	13 feet 1 inch

To complete the comparison of floods during the century, the peak level of 1852 was reported to be one and a half inches below that of the great flood of 1824 and similar to that of 1828.

Unfortunately, the exact location of the gauge and its level (above Ordnance Datum) are unknown, so it is not possible to make direct comparisons with recent floods at the same site. However, an indirect link may be made through a fairly precise knowledge of the level of the 1903 flood at the other side of the city, at Brown's boathouse, upstream from Elvet bridge, where an adjacent staff gauge tells the level of modern floods. The boathouse was built by Mr Ebdy in 1826 after his previous house in Framwellgate had been flooded in 1824. He had only two years to wait before his new property was similarly submerged. It was flooded again in 1852, 1875 and in 1903 when the water was level with the workbench top.

At another site in Durham, the gasworks, it is possible to confirm which were the largest floods. The Gas Company was founded in 1824 and shortly afterwards was supplying gas for domestic and street lighting from its works at Framwellgate Waterside. Apart from the occasions in 1824 and 1828 already noted, only in 1852, 1875 and 1903 did the river reach the level of the retorts and cause a blackout in the city. In 1852 the *Durham Chronicle* reported:

The chandlers shops were beseiged and we had to put our paper to press under a display of candles which would have gratified the devotional yearnings of the most apostolical Puseyite.

One of the town's major industries, the carpet factory, was struck in the same floods. Although a woollen industry was established in the seventeenth century near St Nicholas church in the Market Place, it was not until the business was taken over by Gilbert Henderson in 1814 that it became a thriving carpet manufactory. At its peak in the early 1870s, the business employed five hundred weavers[13]. It was therefore the flood of 1875 which caused most damage, especially at the dye works (more recently the Palace cinema). On Sunday 14 September 1875, workmen moved goods at the dye works all through the day, but had to desist towards 5 p.m. as they were working up to their armpits in water. In the spinning loom department water entered through crevices in the boarded floor and carding machines had to be raised. Even in the lesser flood of March 1881, it was reported that fires were extinguished at the carpet factory.

FILTH COLUMN
As well as the noted industries of the city the poorer folk who lived in New Elvet suffered – not just from the flooding but also from the dubious quality of the water and the consequent dangers to health. Sewers from some houses in Old Elvet simply discharged on to Back Lane and filtered on to the racecourse. The tightly-packed houses in New Elvet had open privies and piggeries backing on to the river. Water Lane, a narrow entry from New Elvet running down to the river, had an open cesspool in the middle of the road, whilst alongside was a lodging house with thirteen or fourteen people to a room[13]. In the mid-ninetenth century New Elvet boasted at least three breweries.

It was across these streets that several of the larger floods swept. In 1852, the racecourse and adjoining gardens were completely covered and all the houses in New Elvet near the Water Lane and in Back Lane were more or less flooded. Twelve hours before the flood peak, police aroused residents at midnight. Mr Petch of the Half Moon inn got his horses out of their stable, whilst carts and pigs were moved at Water Lane.

The local Board of Health started to tackle some of these problems of filth, and from about 1850 began to replace open gutters with sewer pipes.

Householders were themselves required to put in a drain connecting the house to the sewer. The Board's Nuisance Commitee issued abatement orders on piggeries. Nevertheless, the pigsties remained for decades more in New Elvet, and the new drains enabled the flood water to reach places to which surface water had no access. In 1875 the cellars of both the Half Moon and County hotels had several feet of water in them, and in 1903 water came up the drains in Johnson's City brewery and filled the spirit cellar. It also reached the smoke room of the City hotel.

UP AND DOWN THE VALLEY

Outside Durham there were other vulnerable sites, and information on these grew as local newspapers were established in the second half of the nineteenth century.

Along the Wear itself the most frequently flooded buildings were at Page Bank and Sunderland Bridge whilst road flooding at Shincliffe bridge frequently stopped traffic. At Page Bank houses were reported flooded in 1875, 1881, 1886 and 1903. In 1875 only the houses of Old Row escaped and those in New Row were flooded up to their window sills. The Methodist chapel, the school and the Mechanic's Institute were all awash and people were taken out of their houses in 'coup carts'. The Bridge inn at Sunderland Bridge seemed most vulnerable when the Browney was also in spate, as it was in 1875 when the adjoining brewery was submerged and hundred of rats were seen taking to the roof.

There were local differences in flood severity. Thus the snowmelt flood of 10 March 1881 was clearly far more severe in the upper reaches than at Durham. At Stanhope the southern half of the railway bridge collapsed when it was overtopped and, since the gas main crossed the bridge, Stanhope was plunged into darkness. Housed were flooded at The Butts, Unthank mill and Newton, and Shittlehope burn bridge on the way to Frosterley was washed away. Downstream, the ironworks at Witton Park was brought to a standstill as machinery was flooded; two riverside houses at Jock's Row in Bishop Auckland were rendered uninhabitable; and, at Page Bank, colliery mines were flooded. However, the Browney appears to have contributed little to this flood, and its severity diminished downstream.

The floods of 1875, 1886 and 1903, in contrast, gathered strength downstream, with some of the worst problems in lowland tributaries. In 1875 there was severe flooding on the Gaunless, the Browney and the Chester burn. Many houses were flooded in West Auckland from the Gaunless and Oakley Cross beck, and the river swept through the main street of South Church. On the Browney houses were flooded at Lanchester and Wallnook mill and water spread out over a wide area from Stonebridge to Langley. Langley bridge over the Deerness was seriously damaged, Stonebridge inn was flooded and the water was five feet deep at Aldin Grange bridge. On the Chester burn and tributaries, dams, roadways and bridges (including one from Waldridge Fell to Henderson's Drift) were washed away and all the lower part of Chester-le-Street was covered. Wear bridges nearby were impassable. When the flood water receded, the body of a young miner, George Glassey, married just a few days before, was found in the burn at Pelton Fell. A two-year-old child was drowned near Houghton-le-Spring. Flooding at higher elevations was alleviated when the precipitation above a hundred metres turned to snow, but even so, the first reservoir in the Wear catchment, then under construction at Tunstall on the Waskerley beck, suffered severely and downstream High Town in Wolsingham was flooded.

The 1875 flood is commemmorated in a song, 'Sheel Raw Flud' by the 'pitman's poet', Tommy Armstrong, perhaps better known for his north-eastern favourites, 'The Hedgehog Pie' and 'Wor Nanny's a Mazer'. He lived at Tanfield Lea, a mile away from Shield Row to the North of Stanley. The song goes to the same tune as 'The Day we went to Rothesay'.

S'lang as aw live awl nivor forget
One Setorday wen it was se wet,
Ivory body wis nearly bet
Fra th' Setorday till th' Sunda', O!
The ducks did quack an' th' cocks did craw
For wat wis up thae diddent naw,
It neerly droonded awl Sheel Raw,
That nasty Sunda' mornin', O!

Mall Jonson tiv hor husbind sais:
"Reech me ma stockens en ma stais,
For God's suaik let me heh ma clais,
Ot else aw will be droonded, O!"
"Tha clais," said he, "thor guain we mine,
Like Boyd an' Elliot, up the Tyne;
Aw've leukt fra five, an' noo its nine,
This nasty Sunda' mornin', O!"

On the bed she began to rowl,
An flung hor airms around th' powl,
Sa'en, "Lord heh marcy on ma sowl
This nasty Sunda' mornin', O!
Th' vary cats thae ran up staires
Gat on thor nees ta say thor prairs,
Thinkin thae wor gon for fairs
That nasty Sunda' mornin', O!

Aw wis sorry for Sally Clark,
Th' fire wis oot, an' awl wis dark,
She gat oot i' bed wi nowt but hor sark,
That nasty Sunda' mornin', O!
She muaid a splash we sich a clattor,
Thit Bob cried oot, "Sal, what's th' mattor?"
She sais, "Aw's up to me eyes i' wattor,
It must be a nasty mornin', O!"

Bob jump'd oot of he's bed an' awl,
He went where ivor he heerd hor squal,
But th' wattor wis alwis shiften Sal,
That nasty Sunda' mornin', O!
At last th' wattor burst opin th' dor,
An' weshed away buaith Bob an' hor,
At Tinmith they wer wesh't ashore,
That nasty Sunda' mornin', O!

Flood damage in the lowland tributaries was similar in 1886 and 1903. In 1886 there were two fatalities, one in a small stream betwen Kimblesworth and Pity Me and the other in the Bishop Auckland area. Chester-le-Street that year was the scene of particular devastation, with many houses flooded and water swilling through the post office. The embankment round the sewage works burst and the whole works was flooded to a depth of five or six feet within thirty minutes. The same embankment failed in the flood of 1903.

MEMORIES AND PHOTOGRAPHS

After the sequence of floods in the late nineteenth century, the floods of the present century might be regarded as an anticlimax both in terms of severity and frequency. The flood of October 1903 has not been exceeded and, indeed, in the two following decades, only a flood on 18 January 1918, which inundated agricultural land, received the barest mention.

At the turn of the century the first flood photographs appear, and the dramatic shot of Elvet Bridge (Plate 5.3) catches all the power and destructiveness of the 1903 event. Information from newspapers has been supplemented by eyewitness accounts recorded in 1962, and these give information on comparative magnitudes at selected locations.

Thus in 1962, at Brown's boathouse at Elvet, Mr Brown remembered the following levels:

1903	Water reached the top of the 'woodhorse' on which boats are placed whilst repairs are carried out.
1924	Level reached a depth of six inches on the Boathouse floor
1941 }	On both occasions the water just reached the floor
1947 }	level

Several residents at Sunderland Bridge recalled levels in the two earlier floods. Mr Oversby, a newsagent, was working on the new road bridge over the Wear in 1924 and saw the flood of 1 June carry away building materials and damage the foundations. He recalled that the river rose to within one foot of the top of the arch on the Browney side of the old bridge. Older observers agreed that the 1903 flood had reached the top of the arch. Mrs Hall who occupied the Old Bridge house in the 1920s indicated that the water was level with her doorstep

Plate 5.3 Elvet bridge in the flood on 9 October 1903. *Photo. taken from 1 North Bailey by Mr H. P. Robinson*

in June 1924, and again on New Year's Day 1925. Subsequent occupants of the house stated that this level had never again been reached.

The flooding in June 1924 was without historic precedent in that month. Heavy and widespread rainfall is uncommon in June, and soils are usually sufficiently dry to absorb much of what does occur. However, May 1924 was the wettest on record in Durham City and, on the last day of the month, rainfall commenced at 2 a.m. and continued with little variation for forty-three hours till 7 p.m. on 1 June. The total fall for the period was 98.0 mm, whilst the daily total of 70.1 mm, read at 9 a.m. on 1 June, had only been exceeded once in the record since 1841 (on 13 November 1901 when 73.2mm fell).

Between 1903 and 1924 buildings at Elvet may have received some measure of protection as there is little reference to flooding there. Attention was diverted to Framwellgate Waterside where the flood overtopped the cast-iron railing along the riverside wall (Plate 5.4), and residents at the lower end of Castle View terrace and the Sidegate retreated to upstairs rooms. The last house of Castle View was flooded to a depth of four feet.

Flooding along the Gaunless, Browney and Chester burn was again severe. The holiday park at Langley Moor, with its bowling green and tennis courts, was submerged and the road and adjacent houses from Stone bridge to Langley bridge were flooded. A landslip closed the road between Pot and Glass Inn and Aldin Grange. The police station and many houses in Lanchester were flooded from the Smallhope burn. There were two deaths, one a boy of five from

Plate 5.4 Framwellgate bridge from the Waterside 1 June 1924. Note the cast-iron railing to the left, still in existence.

Hunwick station who went with his seven-year-old brother to see the Wear in flood and fell in. The other was a teenage Spennymoor girl who was swept away whilst trying to cross a submerged bridge on a tributary beck.

A principal feature of the New Year's flood of 1925 was the very rapid rate of rise and fall (like the Tees), suggesting an intense burst of rainfall in the midst of a longer period of moderate rain. There was also a strong westerly gale and lightning was observed. The *County Chronicle* reported the flood at Bishop Auckland to be the worst since 1881. The pumphouse at the waterworks was flooded to a depth of three feet and other parts of the works to eight feet depth. Water was two feet deep in two adjoining cottages. Further upriver, a high weir about half a mile west of Wolsingham was partly washed away. Lowland tributaries, however, contributed little and, although houses at Castle View Durham were again flooded, conditions were less severe below the Browney confluence than the previous June.

Except for a minor flood on 13 June 1928, there was little flooding on the main Wear until 1941. However, a localised summer storm centred on the Gaunless on 15 August 1927 wreaked havoc on adjoining villages. At West Auckland an iron bridge was carried away and water rushed down Front Street and Chapel Street to the Market Place. Salisbury Square and the Nursery were also flooded. Water overtopped the banks at Spring Gardens and flowed down Toad Pool and into houses to a depth of three feet. Mr J. Stamper brought out from his home a child's cradle. He got in and, with a stick as an oar, rowed down Toad Pool. At the corner of Front Street, however, the cradle turned a complete somersault, Stamper being hurled overboard.

At St Helen's Auckland, the back lane to Etherley was under water and two bridges near the brewery were covered. At South Church the river was almost level with the top of the bridge arch, and three roads to the village were flooded to nearly two feet.

Because of wartime restrictions, the extraordinary snowstorm beginning on Wednesday 19 February 1941 and continuing for fifty-six hours, and the subsequent floods, were not mentioned in the press until 7 March – and then only very scantily. In Durham City the snow lay two feet deep but elsewhere it was deeper and drifts of fourteen feet were reported. Road and rail traffic came to a standstill for three days and by Thursday there were twenty-five derailments and fifty trains waiting at different places to travel to Newcastle. One thousand soldiers were occupied several days clearing snow and removing poles and wire from the lines. The extent of flooding was not mentioned. The only clues are the observation from Brown's boathouse, and a remark by a resident of 3 Castle View in a later flood in 1947, that the worst flood during her tenancy from 1931 was in 1941 when the water rose two-and-a-half feet in the living room.

Floods in the spring of 1947 followed similar severe snowstorms which were nationally more prolonged and widespread. Even on the coast, Sunderland had forty-one days with snow and temperatures down to −11°C. The thaw and flooding in the rest of England and Wales occurred around 20 March when there was heavy rainfall but in the north the upland snow persisted much longer and the thaw brought flooding on two separate occasions in April. The worst occasion was 21 April when heavy rain fell and gale force winds assisted the thaw. As in the similar winter of 1881, the upland reaches were severely affected. At Stanhope, the Coronation bridge was swept away and houses in the Butts were flooded. The flood peaked in Durham at 11 a.m. when it reached a depth of five feet on Framwellgate Waterside. Tenants at Castle View barricaded their homes with corrugated iron and mud, but to no avail. Mrs Livett who lived at No 3 moved furniture upstairs and told the *Durham Advertiser*:

This is the second time in four weeks. The last occasion was three days before Easter (3 April) and the carpets and lino are not yet dry.

The press reports of flooding in 1947 were brief and doubtless omitted many inundated properties between Stanhope and Durham. The wartime habit of secrecy about the weather had died hard.

RIVERBANK AND CHANNEL CHANGES IN DURHAM

From mid-century changes occurred along the river in Durham, the most significant being at Framwellgate where flood-prone terrace houses were demolished to make way for the new Milburngate shopping precinct and office complex. Castle View and Fowler's Terrace were removed in the early 1960s. However, the cast-iron railing along the riverside wall has survived these changes (as, remarkably, it escaped the World War II demand for munitions), and still provides a guide to the severity of flooding (Plate 5.5).

The bypass created new high-level bridges at Framwellgate and at Elvet where the road carved through the leafy slopes of Paradise gardens. The gardiner's cottage by the river, which had flooded in 1903, was demolished. Woodbine Cottage, on the river bank just below Bath's bridge, went shortly afterwards when a landslip from the new road made it unsafe. At New Elvet, older properties at Water Lane were demolished to provide a site for the University Arts Building and a ground floor car park protected from the river by a floodwall.

Within the river there had been earlier changes to weirs. The ancient Framwellgate weir had for centuries provided the head to operate the bishop's mill. In 1929 the water wheel at the mill was replaced by a turbine to generate electricity for an ice manufacturing plant. The head of water was inadequate and the dam was raised three feet nine inches by stages in 1935 and 1944, and the turbine still provides power to the ice rink. Although this must inevitably have raised flood levels in the reach up to the Museum weir (Fig 5.4) there are no reports before or since of flooding in this reach apart from riverside paths. The Museum weir was breached by ice floes in 1945 but was rebuilt the following year, probably at the same level.

The river channel was widened in 1964 downstream from Framwellgate weir. Berms were formed on the banks at the Sands and a gravel shoal, known locally

Plate 5.5 Framwellgate Waterside Durham 1 June 1924 looking downstream towards Castle View terrace. The line of the top of the railing marks the normal river's edge. Durham Ice Rink now stands across the river on the right bank.

as 'the sludge hump', was removed. These changes are unlikely to have had much effect on flood levels and the flood of 1967 showed that the river had still scope for damaging property.

THE ERA OF RECORDS

The first gauging station in the Wear catchment was set up in 1954 on the river Browney at Burn Hall by adapting an old mill weir. On the Wear itself a gauging structure was built under the arches of the medieval Sunderland Bridge in 1957. Others followed at Stanhope, Witton Park and Chester-le-Street. These have given precise information on river flows and floods for the last three decades[14]. Highest recorded flows at Durham have been obtained by combining the Wear and Browney flows at gauging stations upstream, and are shown in Table 5.2.

Table 5.2 Recorded flows in rank order at Durham since 1957
         (cubic metres per second)

Rank	Date	Flow Sunderland Bridge	Flow Burn Hall	Flow Durham
1	05.11.67	415	43	458
2	26.08.86	324	67	391
3	27.12.78	303	67	370
4	17.10.67	292	28	320
5	28.03.79	239	80	319
6	11.09.76	265	54	319
7	04.01.82	267	42	309
8	15.10.76	264	41	305

Flooding during recent decades has not been exceptional but the flood of 5 November 1967 stands well above the others. The previous month had been unusually wet with a flood in mid-month, which was the fourth highest during the period of records. Although fields and roads were covered in this earlier flood, the principal impact was to saturate the catchment in advance of the November flood. On Sunday 5th, more than 75 millimetres of rain over the greater part of the Wear catchment was accompanied by gale force winds. Floodbanks at Witton, Binchester and Croxdale were overtopped and many breaches occurred.

At Page Bank, the scene of many previous floods, the Wear flowed down riverside fields and into the village, flooding New Row, School Row and West Terrace to a depth of up to five feet before returning to the channel at Page Bank bridge. Twenty residents were evacuated by boat but more retreated upstairs. The bridge support structure was damaged and the bridge was closed (Plate 5.5). After the flood, most of the residents reckoned they had had enough and moved out. The houses became derelict and were, with one exception, demolished in the early 1970s.

At Sunderland Bridge, the Old Bridge house was flooded and at Shincliffe bridge, where much adjoining land and roads were under water, the water rose within eighteen inches of the top of the arches and the bridge vibrated alarmingly. Nearby, part of the Houghall School of Agriculture and the University sports stadium were inundated. Two unorthodox anglers claimed a new record after the flood receded when they caught fifty trout and a salmon in two hours at Durham public bowling green. Locations flooded in Durham are recorded in the Chief Engineer's report to the Northumbrian River Authority (Fig 5.1)[15]:

Bath's boilerhouse	
Brown's boathouse	2 feet
Auto Electrics (Elvet Bridge)	7 inches
McIntyres Garage	6 inches
University Arts Building floodwall	overtopped
Framwellgate: Millburngate House	
(Ministry of Labour)	3 inches
Framwellgate: GPO Savings Dept – basements	
(under construction)	5 feet
Ice Rink: adjoining private house flooded above	
electrical sockets.	4 inches
Royal Observer Corps building	4 inches.

Chester-le-Street the water spread out over the riverside park and reached the A1 (now A167) road. Work was brought to a halt on the nearby motorway bridge, then under construction, but no serious damage was done.

Other floods affected few properties but an exception was the Bridge hotel complex at Sunderland Bridge where forty-six chalets were built at a lower level in the early 1970s. These were all reported to be under nearly two feet of water in the flood of 1986 and they were also flooded in March 1979 when the Browney was at its highest recorded level. (The original inn at the bridge was converted to a dwelling, the Old Bridge house, in the early 1930s.)

The 29 March 1979 flood was severe on many lowland tributaries owing to the initial wet ground conditions caused by a thaw and rainfall on 26 March. Most damage was done on the Chester burn where a culvert collapse led to blockage and then to a surge of water into the centre of Chester-le-Street. The market place and ten commercial properties were flooded (Plate 5.6). Another culvert and roadway were washed away on the Twizell burn.

On the Wear itself the flood between Christmas and New Year in 1978 had been considerably higher and, although no property was affected from the main river, the level caused sufficient alarm at the office complex at Framwellgate for the lower windows of the National Savings building, which gave access to the bank archives, to be blocked up and sealed.

Plate 5.6 Flood water surged through the centre of Chester-le-Street on 29 March 1979 due to combined flooding of the Wear and Chester burn. The inhabitants show there is more than one way to avoid wet feet. *Photo.* Newcastle Chronicle

TREATMENT AND PROGNOSIS

Neither the National Rivers Authority nor its predecessors have carried out major works of flood alleviation on the main river comparable to those on the neighbouring Tyne and Tees. Those floodbanks which do exist were for the most part constructed by landowners to protect their own property, some of them as early as the beginning of the nineteenth century. Reports of the Wear and Tees River Board of the 1950s and early 1960s refer mainly to removal or redistribution of gravel shoals and bank protection or stabilisation[16]. There have, however, been a number of flood alleviation schemes on tributaries. On the Gaunless, the channel was deepened and realigned through West Auckland (1959) and at South Church (1960). The channel of the Browney was cleared and realigned at Langley Moor (1960), whilst work at the troublesome tributary, the Smallhope burn through Lanchester, was done later by Northumbrian Water.

A solution to the flooding problem elsewhere was achieved by the demolition of affected property at Page Bank and Castle View Terrace, Framwellgate. Offices on the latter site have been replaced at a higher floor level but are not entirely without risk, and riverside car parks remain vulnerable.

With the exception of that of 1903 the floods of the twentieth century have not matched the larger floods of the previous century. However, there is no reason to believe that the potential for generating flood flows has altered. Unlike the Tees the Wear has few reservoirs to reduce flood flows. Together Tunstall (constructed 1879) and Burnhope (constructed 1937) have a catchment area of forty-four square kilometres which is less than five percent of the area to Durham. Urbanisation and changes in agricultural practice have not significantly altered the flood runoff process.

The Wear catchment is simply awaiting the right combination of storm rainfall on a wet and perhaps snow-covered catchment to generate its next major flood. Although not much property will be affected, the watchful electronic eyes of the flood warning scheme operated by the National Rivers Authority remain essential.

REFERENCES
1. Beaumont, P. 'Geomorphology', in Dewdney, J. C. (ed), *Durham County and City with Teesside*, (British Association, Durham, 1970)
2. Page, W. (ed.) *The Victoria History of the County of Durham*, (London, 1928), vol. 3, 21
3. Ibid. vol. 3, 64
4. Hodgson, J. C. (ed.), *Six North Country Diaries*, Extracts from The Diary of Jacob Bee of Durham, (Surtees Society no 118, 1910)
5. Durham County. Quarter Sessions Order Books, Bridge Accounts. Mss, Durham County Record Office.
6. Graham, F. *The Bridges of Northumberland and Durham*, (Newcastle upon Tyne, 1975)
7. Hodgson J. C. *op. cit.* The Diary of Thomas Gyll, 1748-78.
8. Smith, L. T. *The Itinerary of England and Wales by John Leland*, (5 vols, London, 1906-10)
9. Richardson, M. A. *Memorials of the Floods*
10. Bell, J. *Account of Floods in 1815 and 1771*
11. Garret, W. *Account of Floods in 1771 and 1815*
12. Kirby, D. 'Lumley Lock: An historical note on an ancient fishery', *Archaeologia Aeliana* Fourth series vol. 47, Society of Antiquaries of Newcastle upon Tyne, (1969)
13. Clack, P. *The Book of Durham City*, (Buckingham, 1985)
14. Archer, D. R. 'Improvement in flood estimates using historical flood information on the River Wear at Durham', *Proc. of the first British Hydrological Society Symposium, Hull,* (1987)
15. Northumbrian River Authority, 'Engineer's Report on the Flood of 5 November 1967', Annual Report 1968
16. Wear and Tees River Board Annual Reports 1951-65.

Plate 6.1 Ashgill Falls on a tributary of the South Tyne near Garrigill, offers the visitor an opportunity to shelter in the overhang behind the fall and to peer through the curtain of falling water.
Photo. D. Archer.

Plate 6.2 The Devil's Water, a Tyne tributary, at Swallowship Hill near Hexham. *Photo. D. Archer.*

6. THE RIVER TYNE

And now the river is rich. A deep choir.
It is the lofty clouds, that work is heaven,
Going on their holiday to the sea.
            Ted Hughes   The River in March   Season Songs

When John Smeaton, the 'father of civil engineering', was approached in 1783 to rebuild the bridge over the Tyne at Hexham he replied:

I would beg you to consider whether you may not stand a better chance by employing some other able Engineer who has not got the Horrors of the River Tyne painted upon his imagination[1,2].

Smeaton's previous bridge at Hexham, commenced in 1777 and completed in 1780, failed in a flood just twenty-one months later. It was the third failed bridge in the reach in little over a decade and it was Smeaton's only serious failure in a lifetime of engineering enterprise and innovation, including the Eddystone lighthouse and the bridging of the Tweed and Tay.

So what was different about the Tyne? Why should the building of bridges on the Tyne (even now) be such a difficult exercise? Modern flood records for the Tyne compared with other rivers of Britain give part of the answer. The 1990 United Kingdom Yearbook of Hydrological Data[3] lists the highest flood flows to be recorded at gauging stations on rivers throughout the country (Fig. 6.1).

The highest recorded flood flow on any river in England and Wales occurred on the river Tyne at Bywell gauging station. It exceeded the highest recorded flow at the furthest downstream measuring point on the Severn, Trent and Thames, with respectively two, three and four times the catchment area contributing to the river. The flow of 1586 cubic metres per second (cumecs) is equivalent to nearly 1600 tonnes of water (since a cubic metre of water weighs one tonne) passing an observer on the bank each second. Historic floods on the Tyne have been even greater than recently measured ones.

If Scottish rivers are included in the comparison, the Tyne flow has been exceeded only by the flashy Findhorn and the Spey in north-east Scotland. The Tay and the Tweed are not far behind the Tyne but have much bigger catchments.

These high flows are associated with very high water velocities. Speeds in excess of five metres per second (eleven m.p.h.) occur in the lower reaches of the Tyne where the flow is unimpeded. Where confined by bridge piers or other structures, the velocity can be much greater. If, as is commonly the case, the bed of the river consists of alluvial material, such speeds can set the whole bed

87

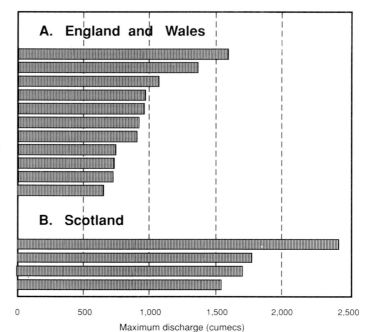

Fig 6.1 Comparison of the highest recorded flood discharge on the river Tyne with that on other British rivers.

in motion. Boulders of several tonnes in weight roll and skip along the bed. Scour holes develop where the flow is confined, especially adjacent to bridge piers, and may undermine the structure.

Topography and climate combine to produce these unusual discharges and velocities. Compared with rivers of similar size, the Tyne has a shorter distance from source to mouth and the channel has a steeper slope. As a consequence the travel time of the flood wave down the channel is short. Intense rainfall over Alston Moor or Kielder Forest may cause the river to rise to its peak level in the lower reaches of the river only eight hours later.

The major tributaries of the North and South Tyne are similar in their characteristics and they contribute almost equally (at least before Kielder Dam was built) to flood flows in the main river downstream from their confluence at Warden (Fig 6.2). The worst condition is when flood peaks from north and south coincide at the confluence.

The headwaters of the South Tyne lie on the northern slopes of Cross Fell and Burnhope Seat adjacent to the sources of the Wear and the Tees. Indeed, from the peat hags of Burnhope Seat, the observer has a splendid view down all three valleys and can stand where the waters part three ways on their journey to the sea. Common plants of these moors are bog cotton and cloudberry whose names suggest the dampness of conditions underfoot and overhead. Storm rainfall has little chance of percolating into the ground and most of it runs off directly to headwater streams and hence to the main river. There are no dramatic waterfalls along the main channel as on the neighbouring Tees, although some steep tributary streams like the Ashgill and Nent reveal hidden splendours (Plate 6.1). For the most part the river flows on a boulder-strewn bed with ephemeral gravel islands separating braided channels. There is a narrow ribbon of floodplain which increases in width downstream. The river Allen, which shares much of the character of the South Tyne, joins it near Bardon Mill.

The North Tyne has its source at the western end of the Cheviot Hills and the watershed separating the Tyne from the Tweed and Liddel drainage systems nearly coincides with the Scottish border. The landscape here is more craggy than in the South Tyne but irregularities are now concealed beneath a blanket of coniferous forest. Kielder Forest occupies five hundred square kilometres, nearly all in the North Tyne catchment, and within it stands Kielder Dam holding back Britain's largest man-made lake, Kielder Water, which stretches eleven kilometres back along the valley. Forest and reservoir have profoundly influenced the landscape and life of the valley; they have also greatly altered the river's propensity for flooding.

In the reach below the dam, the channel gradient slackens a little and the floodplain broadens. Before it was controlled by Kielder Water, the river occasionally spilled on to agricultural land. Below Bellingham the North Tyne is joined by the river Rede which, unlike other major Tyne tributaries, is a broad meandering stream with gentle slopes and a wide flood plain. Below the confluence the valley narrows and steepens again until the meeting with the waters of the South Tyne at Warden.

The principal historic flooding on the Tyne was downstream of this confluence in the string of riverside towns and villages – Hexham, Corbridge, Bywell, Ovingham and Wylam – where the effects were sometimes disastrous. Wylam Bridge now marks the tidal limit, although until the end of the nineteenth century the limit was nearly three kilometres further downstream at Hedwin Streams opposite Ryton. Three important tributaries join within the tidal reach, the river Derwent, whose moorland headwaters rise west of Blanchland, the Team and the Ouseburn.

Extensive dredging of the estuary from about 1855 completely changed the character of the river. In its much deeper channel the river is now confined within its banks even in the most severe flood. In earlier years it spread out across the haughs at Newburn, Blaydon and Lemington and lay deep across the area now occupied by the Metro Centre, 'Europe's largest shopping and leisure complex'. It often inundated the Quayside and adjacent commercial properties and lavish houses of merchants in the lower parts of Newcastle.

In the days before dredging the Tyne had a shallow and tortuous channel right down to the sea. The depth at the bar was a mere six feet at low water. However, it was one of the busiest ports of the realm, where sea-going vessels jostled with keels and other small craft. It is ironic that, on occasions, ships which had survived the storms of the open sea were wrecked or cast ashore on the riverbank as the result of the 'horrors' of the river Tyne.

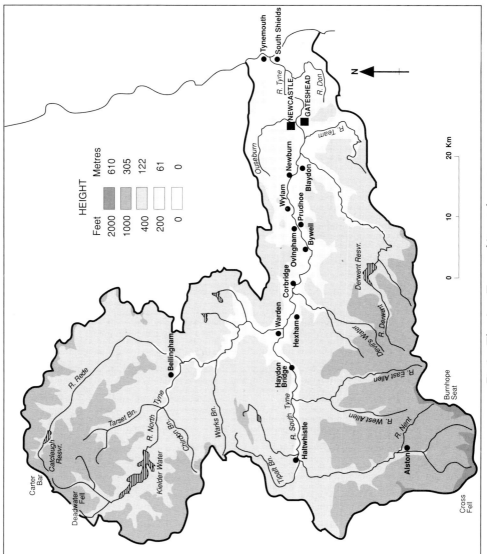

Fig 6.2 The river Tyne and its catchment.

A MEDIEVAL DISASTER

The most disastrous flood on the river Tyne occurred, not in the well-known flood of 1771 but much earlier, on 12 August 1339. The *Chronicle* of Lanercost Priory[4] relates the incident thus:

In the same year on the third day before the Assumption of the glorious Virgin in the night at Newcastle upon Tyne there happened a marvellous inundation of waters whereby the wall of the town near to Walkenowe was broken down for a length of 6 perches and 160 men and 7 priest and more were drowned.

Two editions of Stowe's *Chronicle*[5] give slightly differing accounts. A quarto edition which quotes Rich South states:

AD 1339, An. Reg. 13 Edw. 3d A sodaine inundation of water at Newcastle upon Tine bare downe a piece of the towne wall a six pearches in length neer to the place call'd Wallcrew, where 120 men and women were drowned.

A folio edition again quotes Rich South and a book in the library of St Mary, York:

In the latter end of AD 1338 An. Reg. 12 Edw. 3d the first daye of the Assumption of our Lady, a suddaine innundation of water at Newcastell upon Tine surmounted the wall and bare down a peece of the Towne wall of six perches in length neer to place called Wallknew where 160 men and leaven chaplains and women were drowned.

Although there are discrepancies in these accounts there is no doubt that this was a disaster of the first order. Newcastle at the time was the twelfth in size of English towns but it had a population of less than four thousand (3970 in 1377), and there was therefore a loss of about one in twenty-five of the whole population. One may wonder why such a large proportion of the inhabitants was gathered on a six-perch (thirty-metre) length of the town wall. Almost certainly they had found themselves a grandstand view of the flood in the failing light of a summer evening at a point on the wall nearest to the swirling waters and therefore the most vulnerable to the effects of scour in the soft alluvium beneath the foundations.

And where did the tragedy occur? The variable Wallcrew/Walkenowe/Wallknew settled down to become the Wallknoll, a hillock on the east side of the Pandon Burn surmounted by the Sallyport tower on the town wall and near the present day Manors car park. In the fourteenth century the area had been the property first of the Carmelite friars and later of the House of Trinitarians. It overlooked the river at Sandgate at the lower end of the Quayside and it is most likely near this point, where subsequent floods are known to have impinged, that the disaster occurred.

Brand[6] also notes that in the same flood part of the Tyne bridge was carried away. It remained in a 'ruinous', though probably usable, condition until money was raised for its renovation after 1370.

FURTHER FLOODING BEFORE 1771

No further flood records could be found until the very end of the seventeenth century, when information relating to damage to bridges is recorded in the

Northumberland quarter sessions order books[7]. In a note dated 11 January 1699, an order was made to pay the surveyor forty pounds towards speedy repair of the bridge of Corbridge which had received great damage by the late floods. No cart or wain was to pass until repairs were carried out. Another note dated 8 October 1701 suggests that repairs had not been carried out before the bridge was affected by a second flood:

Whereas the late great floods in the River Tine has very much dampnified Corbridge soe that unlesse speedy care be taken in repairing the same, the said bridge will be in danger of falling down.

With the commencement of printing of regional newspapers in Newcastle in 1711, there is a more comprehensive source of information, but reports are still sparse and relate either to failure of bridges or to more readily observed flooding in Newcastle itself.

The *Newcastle Weekly Courant* of 14 July 1722 reports flooding on the South Tyne on 8 July coinciding with 'Slater's flood' on the river Wear. There was 'an extraordinary fresh' due to heavy rain, the like of which had not been known for many years. Most bridges on the South Tyne were driven down.

On the river Derwent, the Allensford bridge was carried away on the same occasion. It aroused comment in the Durham quarter sessions because, when the bridge had been built thirty to forty years previously, it was agreed that the owner of the property on which the bridge was built would be indemnified against damage, and his house protected. For the loss of a stable and damage to his house, consequent upon failure of the bridge, George Madison, son of the original owner, was granted the sum of £25.

Eleven years later, on 11 December 1733 there is the first reference to flooding of Newcastle Quayside. The *Newcastle Courant* states:

A violent fresh came down the River Tyne, which meeting with the tide, overflowed the keys, entered the cellars, shops and houses of most thereon and has done a great deal of damage.

The flood seems to have centred on the North Tyne where, as recorded in the Warden parish register, 'a great flood broke down Chollerford Bridge'. The eleven-year cycle continued with flooding on Thursday 30 August 1744 when there was said to be a spring tide and a great flood in the Tyne, by which a great number of cellars were filled with water and considerable damage done to many of them.

Summer flooding occurred from 24 to 26 August 1752. The storm was centred on the western end of the Cheviots and most affected the rivers Rede and Coquet. Heavy rainfall persisted for the full two days and was accompanied on the 26th by high winds which together had a devastating effect on the harvest. The flood effects on the main Tyne were less remarkable: the water was described as 'uncommonly high' and 'flooding contiguous low grounds to a great height', but only agricultural land appears to have been affected.

Melting snow with rain and a violent wind, a combination which has since led to repeated flooding on the Tyne, caused the river to be 'swollen to a prodigious height' on 17 February the following year. (Perhaps because of the changes in the calendar and the date of New Year's Day, Richardson mistakenly places this flood a year earlier.) The flood flow and the ebbing tide together resulted in such a strong current that fifteen 'sail of ships' were driven from their moorings, carrying away their mooring rings and the massive rocks to which they were fixed.

Two more bridges were washed away in a flood late in November 1761 centred over the South Tyne: these were the bridges over the Tipalt burn at Glenwhelt (Greenhead) and over the South Tyne at Ridley Hall. The flood appears to have been caused by localised rainfall and no problems were noted at Newcastle.

In the flood of 1 December 1763, on the contrary, there is no information for locations above the city but at Newcastle itself the river was 'at least three feet higher than ever known'. The water rose over the quay late in the evening and spilled through the openings in the town wall. At its peak, it was three feet deep between the wall and Quayside houses, also flooding shops, cellars and warehouses in the Close, Sandhill and Broad Chare. The sloop Billy was driven up on the Quay. Apparently a deep depression had crossed the area, and then become stationary. Associated strong winds were south-east at first but veered north-east later in the day.

For the next decade the flood of 1763 was referred to as 'that remarkable fresh' but, though unusual, this paled into insignificance in comparison to the flood of 17 November 1771.

THE GREAT FLOOD OF 1771

The destructive force of the flood of 1771 was felt throughout the catchment. It was unusual in its wide extent and unique in the historic period in its intensity. Garret[8] reports that of thirteen or fourteen bridges on the Tyne only that at Corbridge remained standing and it was damaged. He lists ten. Of these five were on the South Tyne: Alston, Eals, Featherstone (with a house and a mill), Ridley Hall and Haydon Bridge, and Glenwhelt (Greenhead) on its tributary the Tipalt burn. A wooden bridge at Allendale was swept away and was found intact the next day lying across a lane near Newbrough as if engineered in that position. Only Chollerford is mentioned on the North Tyne and on the main Tyne the new and old alike failed. At Hexham the bridge designed by Gott was demolished just fourteen months after the last stone had been laid, whilst the medieval bridge at Newcastle, though not unmarked by time and tide, had stood over five hundred years. It was opened in 1250, two years after its wooden predecessor and most of the city had been destroyed in a mysterious fire.

The flood swept through the valley during the night of Saturday 16 to Sunday 17, catching sleeping villages unaware and making it more difficult for riverside residents to appreciate their peril. George Jackson who lived at Featherstone Bridge lost most of his household goods and furniture and the rest 'was rendered useless by the said floods which swept away the house in which he lived' (Plate 6.3)[9]. At Bellister opposite Haltwhistle, the farmer Thomas Hetherington lost nine acres of wheat and rye, eight of turnips and fourteen of 'fresh fogg and winter eatage'. 'All his best warm ground is covered with sand and gravel and quite lost and hedges running north and south wracked up and destroyed.' Nearby, the occupant of Bellister Mill lost 'his entire substance'.

Downstream, near the North Tyne confluence at West Boat, a family saved themselves by breaking through the thatch and sat shivering and half naked on the roof-top for many hours. At Hexham, the water swept through the yard of the Spital and laid waste the Tyne Green and adjacent buildings and diverted the mill watercourse. The seven-arch bridge was more than half demolished during the night.

At Corbridge, the floodplain on the southern approach to the bridge probably carried as much water as the river channel and in so doing saved the bridge

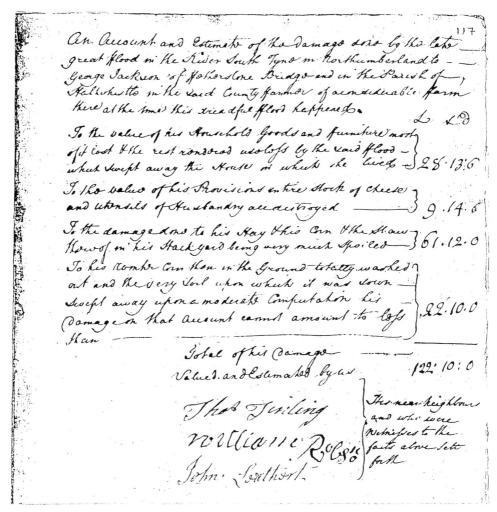

Plate 6.3 An account of the losses by George Jackson of Featherstone bridge, in the great flood of 1771 (from the manuscript record of charity, by permission of the Society of Antiquaries, Newcastle).

from destruction. At the higher northern end of the bridge adventurous souls dangled their arms over the bridge parapet into the swirling water.

The village of Bywell was at that time still a bustling settlement with a street of houses extending from its two churches, St Peter's and St Andrew's, to Bywell Castle. Bywell Hall, which lies to the west of the churches, was then the home of the Fenwick family. It had been completed just five years before to designs by John Paine. It was described at the time as having a lawn before it to the south and a high road along the riverside, lined with statuary which 'on a sunny day are finely imaged by the water'[10]. The latter statement is revealing, for today the river cuts well below the level of the lawn and would give little scope for the observation of such reflected images. At the time, however, the water level was raised, perhaps by as much as three metres, by a substantial weir just upstream from the castle, used both for salmon fishing and to drive a mill[11].

In the early morning of 17 November, the weir was the downfall of the people of Bywell for it caused the water level to back up to an unprecedented level in the Hall, the churches and the village. Garret records that the water stood eight feet deep in the lower floor of the Hall (Bell[12] suggests six feet), and seven feet higher than previously known. The garden walls were all broken down and no doubt the statuary shared the same fate.

By the time the alarm was raised in the village, the water already seemed too deep to allow escape to higher ground and many chose to retreat to their attics and break through their roofs. However, respite was temporary as houses began to crumble beneath their feet. About ten houses were washed away and their inhabitants with them (Plate 6.4). Six people perished but many were saved by holding on to branches of trees as they were swirled down the village street. One infant, Mary Leighton, recently baptised at Saint Peter's, suffered a more severe baptism when her wooden cradle was carried off down river. Miraculously, she escaped total immersion and was rescued safe and well from the sea off Shields more than twenty miles away.

St Peter's church, standing on a slight prominence at the western end of the village and overlooking a bend in the river seemed a suitable retreat for those alerted sufficiently early. Mr Fenwick's servants desperately struggled to bring his more valuable stud horses to this haven. Once inside, however, they found the water still rising and the horses were saved only by standing on pews and even on the altar table. At one time the church itself seemed endangered as the river began to erode the bend on which it stood. The churchyard wall was ruined and 'dead bodies and coffins were torn out and the living and the dead promiscuously clashed in the torrent'. The church itself survived, though like its sister church it was much damaged.

The greater part of the village of Ovingham, the next downstream, was less vulnerable. It stands on a raised terrace above the river and is dominated by the medieval church and its Saxon tower. Like Bywell, it too had a weir, though a much lower one, sited just downstream from the present bridge. A ferry plied across the river on the pool created by the weir between a jetty on the Prudhoe side and the ferry landing steps on the Ovingham side. The weir has long since

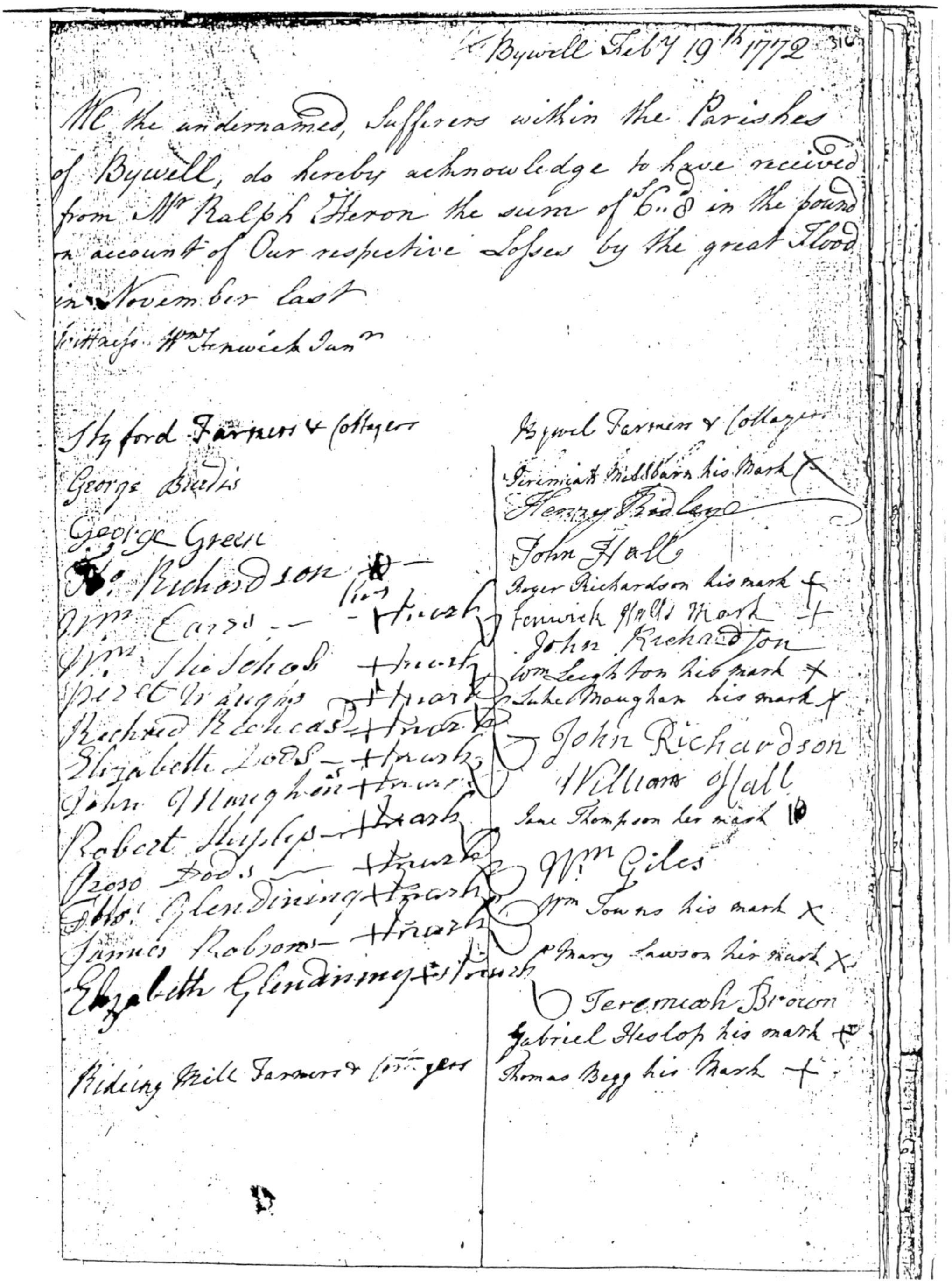

Plate 6.4 The record of charitable payments to sufferers in the great flood of 1771 at Bywell and Styford (from the manuscript record of charity, by permission of The Society of Antiquaries, Newcastle).

gone but the timbers of the jetty can still be seen exposed at low water and the steps still provide access to the riverbank footpath.

Near the foot of these steps stood the boathouse, by far the lowest building in Ovingham. Unfortunately, on the night of 16 November there were ten people in the house, John Johnson the boatman, his wife and two children, his mother and brother Matthew, a man and maid servant, a young visitor from Prudhoe and a labourer called George Simpson. They, too, were taken unawares and though the safety of the high riverbank lay just behind the house they were already cut off by the rapidly rising floodwaters. They ascended by stages to the upper floor, then to the attic, then broke through the end wall into the stable. They remained there for some time but eventually, as the dwelling house began to give way, they climbed out on to the stable roof and three of them, Matthew Johnson, the young visitor and George Simpson clung to the chimney top. Suddenly the whole structure collapsed and they were thrown headlong into the torrent. As John Johnson was carried downriver he snatched at the overhanging willows. He finally managed to catch a projecting branch with one hand and grasp his wife with the other, but she was torn from him by the strength of the current. Two others, the boatman's brother and the maid, also became lodged in the trees where all three remained for ten hours until eleven o'clock on Sunday before they could be relieved. The maid died shortly after she was brought to shore, bringing the total loss to eight. Their deaths are recorded in the Ovingham parish register (Fig 6.5).

At Wylam the loss was material rather than human. The three-hundred-acre coal workings were completely flooded and the damage was estimated at more than £800. In the tidal reach, too, many houses were deeply inundated. At Newburn the boathouse, now a public house, was flooded to the ceiling of the ground floor. The level, by far the highest ever reached, has been recorded on an engraved stone in the wall. At Swalwell families were rescued by boat from their upper storeys.

In Newcastle all riverside properties from the west end of the Close to near Ouseburn were under water and even on the Sandhill boats plied on water six feet deep. The quayside was swept clean of merchandise and three sloops and a brig were stranded there, furrowing up the pavement. Other craft, large and small, were driven away from their moorings and scattered on each side of the river to Shields and out to sea.

However, the most significant action was taking place on the Tyne bridge, at the time the only crossing between Newcastle and Gateshead. Although the bridge had stood firm for five centuries it was vulnerable to an extreme flood for a number of reasons. Firstly, the massive piers restricted the natural waterway, occupying a little over a third of the cross section. The sterlings on which the piers rested occupied an even greater proportion (54 percent) at low water. Ballast-dumping downstream of the bridge, both accidental and deliberate, further reduced the free flow. Secondly, the practice of building over the bridge reduced the stability in high flows, especially on the Gateshead side where shops and dwellings were continuous over the arches as well as the piers.

The maintenance of the bridge suffered from divided responsibilities. The

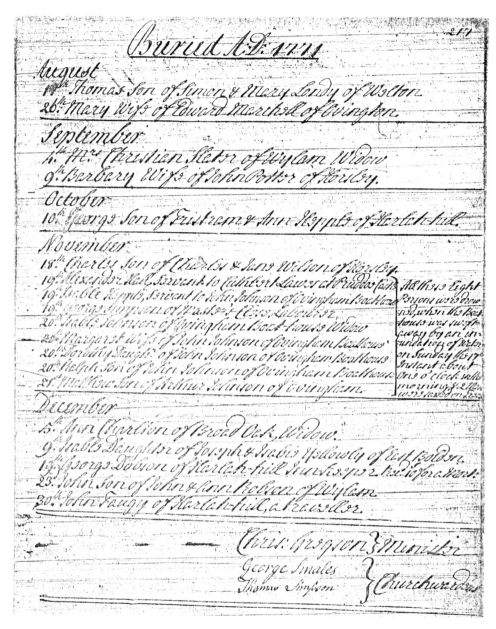

southern end (three-and-a-half piers and four arches) had since 1417 belonged to the Bishops of Durham whilst the remainder (five-and-a-half piers and six arches) was owned by the City of Newcastle. Bridge upkeep was a contentious issue throughout its life[13]. The engineer John Smeaton had been engaged for an inspection in the 1760s. He had reported some arches in danger of falling and had recommended the replacement of the bridge. However, each side continued to make its repairs independently, the last being completed on the Gateshead side as recently as May 1771.

Mr Fiddes, who occupied with his family a house on the Newcastle end of the bridge, was the first to be alerted to danger at three o'clock in the morning of 17 November. He chose to escape southward to Gateshead. He had reached safety with his wife, two children and maid, Ann Tinkler, when the latter persuaded him to return with her to retrieve some valued possessions. He reluctantly agreed and, as his wife stood watching anxiously for his return, she saw them suddenly disappear from view as the first arch collapsed. Ironically, his house survived.

Meanwhile Peter Weatherley, in his home above his shoemaker's shop, awakened and saw the Fiddes family passing below for the first time. He was considering his own response when the arch to the north of his house fell. In haste he roused his family and on opening the door found the water rolling by just below. As they attempted to escape southward with the pavement crumbling beneath their feet, they were horrified to find that two other arches had fallen. The gaps were still bridged on the east side by the remnants of houses precariously perched on timber beams but their path was cut off and they were stranded on a surface only six feet square which threatened to be engulfed at any moment. There Weatherley, his wife, two children and servant girl remained for six interminable hours. They saw the water rise to its highest at seven o'clock in the morning and then gradually recede.

They were rescued by the heroic efforts of a Gateshead bricklayer, George Woodward. He broke a hole through the side of each shop from the Gateshead end, all the way to where they were trapped, and guided them back through the openings. Later in the day four of these houses with shops collapsed into the river and the remaining houses on the Gateshead side had gone by the end of the month. Apart from the central arch, the Newcastle end of the bridge remained intact (Plate 6.6).

Three other bridge residents perished in the flood, Christopher Byerley, a hardware merchant, and his son, and a young apprentice cheesemonger. Two others died shortly afterwards as a result of the shock.

At Newcastle the flood was said to have risen twelve feet above high water spring tide level (6.0 to 6.5 metres above Ordnance Datum). However, downstream the floodwaters rapidly dissipated and at Hebburn and South Shields the level was not much higher than a normal spring tide.

Shortly after the flood a charity was set up under the administration of the clergy, for the relief of victims[9]. The committee was responsible for compiling a register of sufferers and the extent of their loss, and of distributing funds. A summary of losses by parishes in Northumberland is shown in Plate 6.7.

Plate 6.6   Brand's drawing of Newcastle bridge after the 1771 flood (by permission of Newcastle City Library).

BRIDGE FAILURE AT HEXHAM

Although a bridge at Hexham across the Tyne may have existed in the thirteenth century, it cannot have stood for long as from the fifteenth to the late eighteenth century it is known that the means of crossing was by a ford or ferry. However, these were unsatisfactory or even dangerous, either because of high water levels and velocities or because of the rapid rate of rise. The steep wave front on the Tyne could sometimes match that on the river Tees. In 1766 a summer flood wave 'rolled a yard perpendicular'. A woman was drowned crossing stepping stones on the South Tyne and several bathers were left without clothes. Later the same year a man was drowned attempting to ride the ford at Hexham.

The need for a bridge at Hexham became greater with growing industry and transport after the middle of the eighteenth century. In particular, the Alemouth Turnpike (Act of Parliament 1752), which ran from Hexham to Alnmouth, still depended on the ford at Hexham although it was able to use existing bridges at other river crossings.

In 1764 Sir Walter Blackett, who owned the estate of Hexham Abbey, invited John Smeaton to design a bridge for Hexham but he was busy elsewhere and John Gott was engaged[14]. Gott designed a seven-arch bridge for a site about a

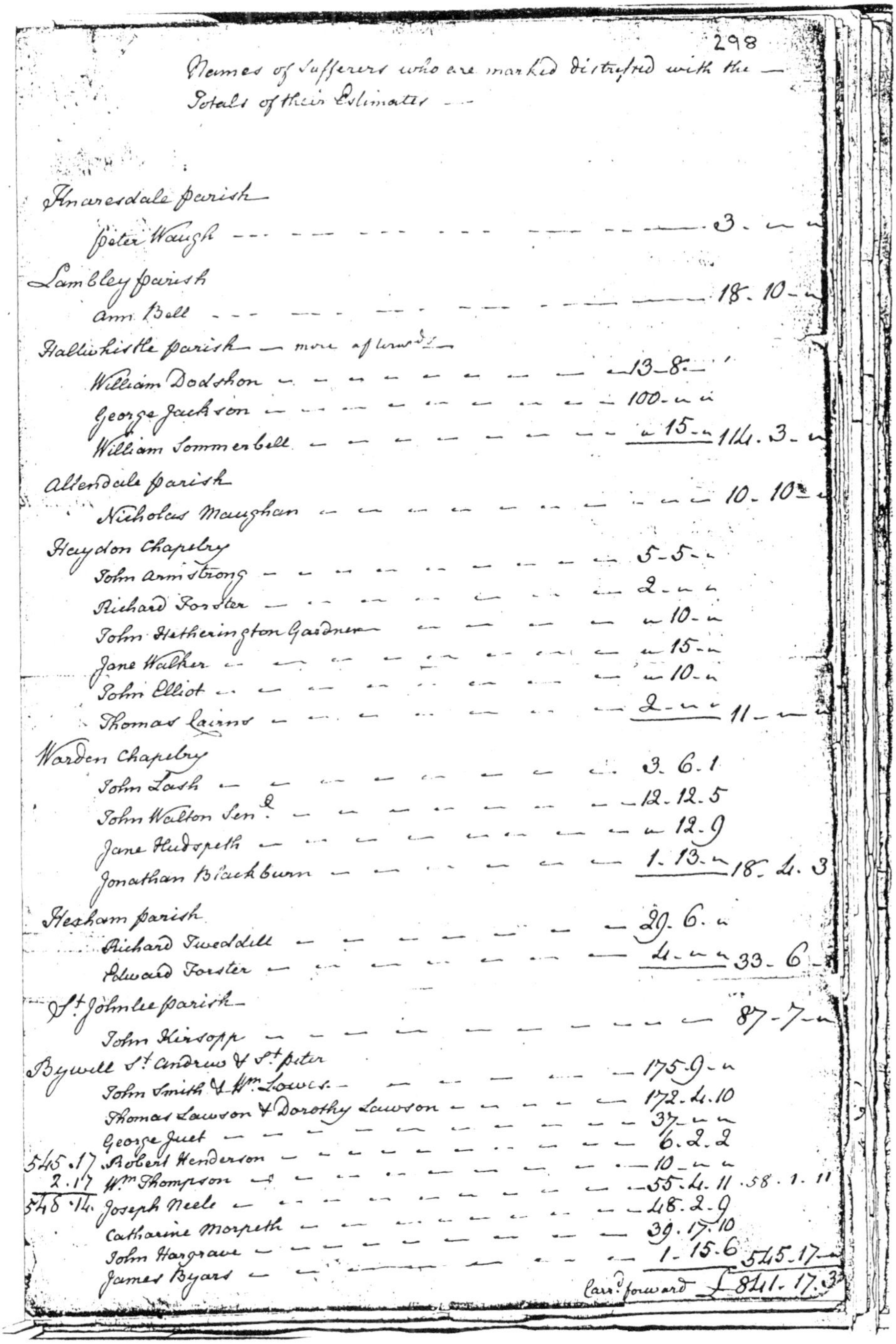

Names of Sufferers who are marked distressed with the —
Totals of their Estimates —

Hinaresdale parish
   Peter Waugh --- -- -- -- --- --- --- 3. —

Lambley parish
   Ann Bell --- -- -- --- --- ——— 18. 10 —

Hallitestle parish — more afterwds
   William Dodshon — — — — — — — 13-8-
   George Jackson — — — — — — — — 100 — —
   William Sommerbell — — — — — — — — 15 — 114. 3. —

Allendale parish
   Nicholas Maughan — — — — — — — 10. 10 —

Haydon Chapelry
   John Armstrong — — — — — — — 5-5- —
   Richard Forster — — — — — — 2 — —
   John Hetherington Gardner — — — — 10- —
   Jane Walker — — — — — — 15- —
   John Elliot — — — — — — — 10. —
   Thomas Cairns — — — — — — — 2 — — 11 —

Warden Chapelry
   John Tash — — — — — — — 3. 6.1
   John Walton Sen d — — — — — — 12.12.5
   Jane Hudspeth — — — — — — 12.9
   Jonathan Blackburn — — — — — 1. 13. — 18. 4. 3

Hexham parish
   Richard Tweddell — — — — — 29. 6. —
   Edward Forster — — — — — 4 — — 33. 6

St Johnlee parish —
   John Kirsopp — — — — — — 87-7- —

Bywell St Andrew & St Peter
   John Smith & Wm Lowes — — — — 175.9 —
   Thomas Lawson & Dorothy Lawson — — 172.4.10
   George Juet — — — — — — 37 — —
   Robert Henderson — — — — — 6.2.2
545.17   Wm Thompson — — — — — 10 —
2.17   Joseph Neele — — — — — 55.4.11 .58. 1. 11
548.14   Catharine Morpeth — — — — 48.2.9
   John Hargrave — — — — — 39.17.10
   James Byars — — — — — 1. 15.6 545.17 —
   Carr.d forward £ 841. 17. 3

Plate 6.7 A summary of losses by those designated 'distressed' in the parishes of Northumberland (from the manuscript record of charity, by permission of the Society of Antiquaries, Newcastle).

kilometre upstream from the present bridge. The foundations consisted of tapered timber piles driven three to four metres into the bed, supporting a platform of timbers set one metre below the river bed. The masonry piers rested on these platforms. The bridge was commenced in October 1767 and was almost complete in 1769. After some delays in diverting the approach roads to the bridge ends, Blackett laid the last stone on 29 September 1770.

As noted earlier Gott's bridge was one of the many that failed in November 1771. John Gibson of Sandhoe[15] described the scene shortly afterwards:

On the said night it was totally demolished. Where five of the piers which supported the well turned arches, stood erect, only little hurrocks of stones are lying. When I viewed the ruins, I did not see so much as any of the sixth, nor of the land-breast on Hexham side; neither any vestiges of the arches lying: a great part of the north land-breast was standing, but very much shattered.

As the bridge collapsed during the night, and was not observed, there was some speculation about the mode of failure. One possibility was that the bridge was submerged and simply pushed over by the momentum of the water and the debris contained. However, Smeaton also found evidence that scour had undermined some piers, by taking off an armouring layer of gravel and exposing a weaker layer of sand. He suggested that the driving of piles had contributed to the weakening of this crust, citing in evidence the platform of one of the piers which was found tilted at forty-five degrees to the horizontal. The remains of the timber piling from Gott's bridge can still be seen in the river, now projecting well above bed level because of gravel removed during the 1950s and 1960s.

As a consequence of the failure, Blackett forfeited a bond of £3000 which he had made to maintain the bridge for seven years after its completion. With this money and the materials from the first bridge, the County Justices were anxious to secure a replacement. They engaged a local engineer, John Wooler, who after preliminary site investigations commenced the foundations for his first pier in 1774, fifty metres upstream from Gott's bridge. The resident engineer, Jonathan Pickernell, was horrified at what he found: 'quicksand full of bubbly springs and of so loose a texture that, by hand only, a bar of iron entered into it 46 feet without meeting any resistance'.

Wooler immediately abandoned his plans and suggested that, if a bridge were to be built at all, it required a foundation 'wall' two metres high and thirteen metres wide across the full width of the river, with timber piling upstream and downstream. The proposal was too expensive for the county and was not taken up. Instead, they financed further site investigations, throwing their net rather wider. A suitable site was found downstream and, with the support of Henry Errington within whose estate the new site lay, John Smeaton was again approached and this time agreed to accept the job.

Smeaton, after investigating the first failure, considered it essential to leave the gravel crust undisturbed. The piers were to be founded in caissons and the base of the central piers was to rest directly on the river bed. For defence against scour, the base of each pier would be surrounded by a girdle of large rocks each greater than a tonne in weight. For the piers next to the abutments, where the gravel was deeper, he decided that the usual method of cofferdams with bearing piles would be acceptable.

By the early summer of 1778 the foundations of four piers had been completed and brought up above water level, but as yet were without the rubble protection, when a flood of modest proportions scoured the bed and caused the piers to tilt and settle by as much as half a metre. Smeaton was obliged to reconsider his design. He added sheet piling in front of each pier and extended the area of rubble protection. Building of the piers continued with adjustments for the tilting and the bridge was completed and opened on 1 April 1780.

The people of Hexham, who had by now grown accustomed to the early failure of their bridges, were quickly on the scene with each flood to view its collapse. However, after a year and a half they had almost given up the exercise when disaster struck. The cause was snow on the evening of 10 March 1782 followed by heavy rain and violent winds the next morning. On the South Tyne the rebuilt bridges at Featherstone and Ridley Hall were carried away, Haydon bridge became impassable and on the West Allen a bridge at Whitfield was destroyed. On the North Tyne a man was drowned at Simonburn.

At Hexham, John Donkin, Errington's agent, went down to inspect the bridge in the early morning. Donkin's son and some workmen crossed over and had just returned reporting 'all safe' when they observed particles of lime beginning to fly from the fourth arch from the north end. In little more than a minute, a crack appeared in the arch; it grew wider and spread across the spandrel between the third and fourth arch. In a minute more, two arches and the pier collapsed together. Within half an hour, all but two of the arches had fallen and these followed in the evening. The middle piers (directly on the gravel) were tilted, with their upstream ends sunk in the bed and the downstream end lifted above it (Plate 6.8). The side piers built on piles fared no better.

The velocity of water had been sufficient to dislodge the girdle of large rocks and expose the foundations to the full force of the current. Indeed, the rubble may well have contributed to channelling and thus increasing the velocity. In a modern analysis, Ruddock[14] calculates mean velocity between the piers at 6.84 metres per second with the possibility of even higher figures adjacent to the upstream shoulders of the piers. Smeaton simply misjudged the flood potential of the river Tyne.

Several years of litigation followed in which Robert Mylne was engaged to report on the failure and then to supervise the rebuilding of the bridge[16]. His involvement in design, however, was probably confined to the foundations, for the superstructure as it stands today is largely a replica of Smeaton's design and is on the same site. His foundation design had moved some way towards Wooler's 'wall'. The bed was paved (framed and sett) across the full width of the river from two metres upstream to five metres downstream from the piers, and the blocks were held in place by five lines of closely spaced piles right across the river. A weir downstream raised water levels but lowered velocities through

HEXHAM BRIDGE, AFTER THE FLOOD.

Plate 6.8   The ruins of Smeaton's Hexham bridge after the flood of 10 March 1782
(from Richardson, Memorials of Floods).

the arch and enabled much of the energy to be dissipated downstream rather
than on the bridge itself.

The bridge was thoroughly tested during construction by summer floods in
1792. On 16 July thunderstorms were centred over the North Tyne and Rede
and, on the latter, levels were one foot higher than in 1771. In the Bellingham
area, a bridge and several mills were carried away and a bridge at an unspecified
location on the Hexham to Carlisle turnpike was also destroyed. The bridge
was completed in 1793 and has stood for nearly two centuries. It has not yet
had to contend with a flood of the magnitude of that of 1771 but it has
weathered several floods equal to or a little greater than that of 1782. Plate 6.9
shows Hexham bridge surviving the flood of January 1955, the largest of the
twentieth century. In contrast, Plate 6.10 shows the majestic proportions of the
bridge, etched by the evening sun through the arches, in low flow conditions.

More recent bridges over the Tyne at Hexham have not been without their
problems. The Border Counties railway bridge, which crossed the Tyne
obliquely upstream from the Spital, was damaged during construction in
September 1856. A century later it suffered serious damage in the floods of 1947,
though it was explosives that finally demolished the bridge when Beeching
decided it had reached the end of its useful life. A few hundred metres upstream,
the Constantius bridge, built to carry the A69 dual carriageway Hexham by-
pass, has had a short but chequered history. When building was in progress,
the formwork for the piers was washed away by a summer flood in August
1975 causing serious damage to the structure. Since completion it has continued

to suffer settlement and scour around the piers, and remedial works have cost a significant proportion of the original cost of the bridge.

THE SNOWMELT FLOOD OF 1815

Over the next two decades the river was quiescent with one mention of a flood on 5 September 1807, which originated on the North Tyne and caused agricultural losses. However, in mid-December 1814, the river gave a hint of its continuing virulence. Snowfall on 10 December was followed by rain on the 16th, accompanied by a 'great hurricane' from the south-west. On the North Tyne and Derwent several dam heads were reported to have been carried away and the *Chronicle* notes that 'there has not been so great a flood in the North Tyne since 1771'. However, on the main Tyne the damage was confined to agricultural land.

The same succession of events was repeated a year later, though in much exaggerated form, to produce what was undoubtedly the greatest flood since 1771. Snow lay on the hills from 17 November and was augmented by a terrible snowstorm on 20 December. On that occasion two men perished in the snow near Alston. One of these, a postman, was overwhelmed on his way from Penrith to Alston, a tragedy the more marked because his father had similarly died in a storm two years before. The severe weather continued until the evening of the 28th when the thaw started with rain continuing all next day.

Towards the evening [29 Dec.] the wind began to blow with great violence from the westward and southwest. During the course of the night the gale increased in a most alarming and excessive degree, and particularly towards midnight when it blew with all the force of a tornado. The immense accumulations of snow in the hills, being suddenly melted through the united powers of the thaw and wind, the River Tyne was swelled to an extraordinary height[12].

Several bridges on the South Tyne again succumbed. At Knarsdale, Eals bridge was carried away and at Haydon Bridge two arches fell at 9 p.m. being 'too low to admit the volume of water'. Two hours later, the Glenwhelt bridge on the Tipalt burn lost one arch. However, Robert Mylne's bridges at Hexham and Ridley Hall stood firm as did his Chollerford bridge on the North Tyne.

At Corbridge, the bridge was impassable as floodwaters surged around the south end, and the first man to cross at eight in the morning of 30 December still had to ride up to the saddle in water. The flood again swept through Bywell village and 'reached within four inches of the threshold of the castle'. At Wylam, the cast-iron colliery railway was 'much injured' and a great part of it 'entirely destroyed'.

Conditions were no better in the upper tidal reach. At Newburn and Scotswood, residents had to be rescued by boat through roofs and windows. Some house walls were washed down at Lemington and Dunston but one resident of Lemington did not let a little dampness spoil his social plans:

Water rose to a depth of five feet at Mr Bone's house where an annual club dinner was to be held that day. The dinner was cooked and taken to the house. Guests entered through upper windows by a ladder.

Plate 6.9 Hexham bridge designed by Robert Mylne, and completed in 1793, during the largest flood of the twentieth century on 10 January 1955. Photo. Evening Chronicle.

The Tyne again overtopped its banks at Newcastle and, at the flood peak at 5 a.m., the quay and the lower part of the Close were inundated. Cellars storing sugar and other dry goods were filled with water. The new bridge (opened in 1781 to replace that lost in 1771) seemed endangered, as several arches became choked with ice, timber and keels. The second arch from the north side was almost completely closed with a keel fixed lengthwise across. The trapped keelmen's cries for help were heard by James Craig who put off in a small boat and, with the help of a youth, managed to transfer the men. But on their return the boat was swamped in a strong eddy and, although the keelmen survived, their two rescuers were drowned.

Lives were also lost at Shields where more than thirty vessels drifted from their moorings and on to Herd Sand or out to sea.

FLOOD LEVEL STONES – NEWBURN BOATHOUSE TELLS A TALE

The practice of engraving the flood level on tablets of stone, set in gardens or house walls, seems to have started on the Tyne with the 1771 flood. It was perhaps born of the notion that, unless recorded in some permanent form, future generations would consider stories told of the flood to be fishermen's tales. Indeed, if only a single stone survived we would still find it difficult to credit the level recorded. In fact, five 1771 flood stones have been located and these seem generally consistent. At four of these sites there are also stones

Plate 6.10 The river Tyne at Hexham bridge in calmer mood showing downstream weirs. *Photo. D. Archer.*

Plate 6.15 Low Prudhoe on 17 October 1967 with playing fields and ICI works flooded. The site is now occupies by an industrial estate, with a Kimberly Clark factory, and a sewage works, and protected by a floodbank. *Photo. Douglas Mannear.*

marking the 1815 flood level and at a Newburn boathouse, now a public house, there are three further stones, providing a chronology through to the middle of the nineteenth century.

West Boat (NY 912659) This 1771 stone was built into the wall of the old Boathouse Inn on the south bank of the South Tyne, just upstream from the confluence. The Inn is now a ruin and the stone is covered in a tangle of ivy. However, the inscription is clear – perhaps too clear – and there is a suspicion that the stone replaced an earlier one. In reporting a flood in 1924 the *Hexham Courant* stated that the flood stone at West Boat was almost indecipherable. This stone seems a little lower than the others in relation to subsequent floods. A short distance away, on the Acomb side of the confluence (NY 919661), an 1815 flood stone was recently uncovered from the undergrowth.

Hermitage Mill (NY 934652) A square block of stone without inscription, set in the field to the north-east of the mill, is said by Miss Bettine Morant of the Hermitage to mark the 1771 level. The level of the 1815 flood is inscribed on the mill's south wall and, at a lower level, a 1926 floodmark is etched.

The Hermitage (NY 936651) Two tablets etched with 1771 and 1815 levels are embedded in the shrubbery on the north side of the drive. The inscriptions are faded but are still readable in the right light.

Ovingham Old Vicarage (NZ 085636) Flood stones clearly marked 1771 and 1815 are set in the terraced garden wall of the vicarage adjacent to the steps overlooking the river.

Newburn: The Boathouse pub (NZ 164653) The quoin stones of the pub are marked with a sequence of levels (Plate 6.11) reading from the top 1771, 1815, 1832, 1856 and 1852. The 1771 level is 2.46m above the road level outside and 8.42m above Ordnance Datum at a point within the tidal reach of the river.

Although the engraved stones of the Boathouse seem to provide a precise chronological record there is one small detail which casts some doubt on their precision if not on the occurrence of flooding. A careful search uncovered no evidence whatever of flooding in 1832 although, on 9 February of the previous year, the Tyne with major rivers to north and south (notably the Tweed and Yorkshire Ouse) suffered another severe snowmelt flood accompanied by strong south-westerly winds. All houses on flat land from Newburn downwards were under water and the flood reached roof level in parts of Dunston. The Quay and Sandhill were again covered. There is no doubt that this is the flood referred to by the stone, but the wrong year suggests that the stone was set in place long after the event, perhaps at the same time as one of the later stones.

Nor is the information necessarily comprehensive. A search of records suggests that other floods between 1815 and 1856 may have had a severity to match the lower of those recorded by the flood stones. Flooding of Newcastle Quayside was also reported in 1825 (2 Feb.), 1827 (27 Feb.), 1829 (13 Oct.), 1834 (10 Jan.), 1837 (10 Jan.), 1841 (7 Oct.), 1845 (3 Oct.), and 1846 (8 Aug.),

Plate 6.11 The Boathouse Inn, Newburn, with flood stones showing flood levels in 1771, 1815, 1832, 1856 and 1852. *Photo. D. Archer.*

although here the level would have been influenced to some extent by the accompanying tide and in one case, 1825, the flooding was entirely tidal.

The severity of these and other floods can be only approximately gauged, as newspaper and other comments tend to be insufficiently specific with respect to location or level reached. On Christmas Day 1824 villages adjacent to the river were all 'more or less inundated' and water was seven feet deep in a house at Blaydon. At Corbridge, the water was so deep round the south end of the bridge that the horses had to swim with the True Briton coach. On 27 February 1827, houses were again flooded in the upper tidal reach, and people were rescued from their houses by boat. At the Quay, water extended at least fifty yards up Broad Chare and Alexander Brodie, the oldest wherryman, amused spectators by plying a small boat on the Quay.

On some occasions only one branch or tributary was in flood. The Derwent and Team were affected by a summer flood of 13 July 1828. On the Derwent a paper mill was damaged at Shotley Grove and wooden bridges were washed away at Lintzford. Later that year, although the *Chronicle* proclaimed the flood of 2 December 'the highest since 1815', the South Tyne was unaffected. All the haughs east of Hexham were reported under water. At Townley Main Colliery the river overflowed old workings and broke into the Star Flat pit, drowning one man and fourteen horses. Although a paper mill and workmen's cottages were flooded at Scotswood, there is no reference in this event to Quayside flooding.

It was around this time that preparations were being made for the construction of the Newcastle and Carlisle railway, and the occurrence of flooding, and in particular the 1828 flood, had a strong bearing on its alignment and level[17]. The riverside route along the Tyne had been favoured for its low gradients but, in seeking parliamentary approval for the scheme, strong objections were raised on account of its susceptibility to flooding. Benjamin Thompson, who was promoting the line through Parliament, admitted that in an ordinary flood ten miles, and during a severe flood possibly more than fifteen miles, of railway might be under water for up to twelve hours. However, the line received parliamentary approval largely in its original course, and construction commenced in 1830. Most of the suggested sites of flooding were along the tidal river, and events over the next half century confirmed Thompson's forecast.

The following year on 24 July it was the turn of the South Tyne which 'rose to a height not reached since 1815 if it was higher even then'. On this occasion a prolonged thunderstorm with flash floods caused more damage on small tributary burns than on the main river.

On 14 October 1829, there was a flood from more general rainfall and on the main Tyne this was again said to be the highest since 1815. At Hexham, Tyne Green was covered and the lower rooms of many houses were under water. A woman was drowned at Wylam. At Scotswood, where the new suspension bridge was under construction, scaffolding for the south abutment was carried away and the embankment approach road was breached. Agricultural losses were considerable and there were reports of sheep, cattle, asses and horses being washed down. Cellars at Quayside and the Close were penetrated with much loss of goods and liquors.

There was another localised flood on the upper South Tyne on 21 November 1833. The west abutment of the new, one-arch masonry bridge under construction at Alston was undermined and the arch collapsed.

The flood of January 1837 followed a two-week period of frost and an accumulation of snow, the most severe since 1823. The thaw was rapid and accompanied by rain. The most serious damage was recorded at Scotswood, where fourteen houses were flooded to a depth of five feet, and at Dunston where water reached chest height in a number of cottages. There is a precise indication of the level reached at Bywell where the new stone bridge was being built. A dispute had arisen between the county surveyor and Mr T. W. Beaumont of Bywell Hall and his bridge architect, concerning the level and flood capacity of the bridge[18]. Construction commenced and foundations were laid in 1836 before the surveyor had seen the plans. From local information he determined that the 1815 flood level would have risen dangerously close to the bridge soffit. The flood of 1837 was four feet six inches below the 1815 level but still two-and-a-half feet above the springing of the arches. The county required an additional bridge elevation of five feet and, when the builder failed to comply, they refused to adopt it as a county bridge. Mr Beaumont and his son were obliged to maintain the structure until 1880 when it was finally adopted[19]. It is interesting to note that the piers of an ancient (probably Roman) bridge, which lay just upstream from the present bridge, were demolished when the new bridge was begun[20]. This was to permit a smoother approach during flood flow, but no doubt the material was also used for the rubble infill for the new bridge spandrels.

Floods in 1839 and 1841 caused much damage in North Northumberland but were only locally serious in the Tyne catchment. That of 15 September 1839 mainly affected the Rede and Otterburn where a dam failed (Chapter 10) and on 7 October 1841 the Derwent was reported to be at its highest level since 1771. The bridge at Blanchland was broken and that at Allensford badly damaged. Derwent and Team were again affected in September 1852 in a storm centred on the River Wear. Team valley was 'altogether submerged' with only the tops of hedges visible, and at Shotley Bridge on the Derwent a weir was carried away. Water was several feet deep in the gatekeeper's lodge at Axwell Park.

October 1845 marks the last entry of Richardson's pioneering chronicle of floods in Northumbria[21]. He gives an elaborate account of losses to shipping at the Quay and at Shields owing to the high velocity of the current. Several miles of the Newcastle to Carlisle railway were under water, including Blaydon station which was knee-deep.

And so, by way of many storms, we return to the floods of Newburn Boathouse in 1852 and 1856. These were undoubtedly major floods, although contemporary descriptions, in contrast to the marks, seem to suggest that the flood of 11 December 1852 was the larger of the two. The *Newcastle Journal*, with uncertain memory, records the 1852 flood as the highest for 18 years:

From Redheugh up to Newburn the river presented one immense sheet of water, the Derwent and Blaydon haughs being entirely submerged and the houses and manufactories at these places as well as at Dunston, Blaydon, Scotswood and Lemington were so far inundated that in many cases the inhabitants had to seek refuge on the rising ground or in the upper part of their dwellings. The Scotswood Road near Paradise was fully four feet under water. Above Scotswood Suspension Bridge two paper mills were flooded to a depth of one to two feet. Cottages at the foot of the Scotswood railway station were flooded to four or five foot depth. The ferry boat was washed away at Benwell. The train leaving Central Station at five o'clock had to force its way into Blaydon Station against a current 1 1/2 feet deep running like a mill race. The train proceeded as far as Riding Mill where part of an embankment had given way and passengers were obliged to return to Newcastle.

In renewed flooding just five days later, a new railway bridge at Haltwhistle on the South Tyne carrying the Alston branch was swept away.

It is unclear which of the two floods in 1856 is marked by the Newburn flood stone. That of 28 September was proclaimed with profound imprecision, 'one of the highest floods that occurred within almost living memory'. The level was recorded on another flood mark on the upstream north abutment of Bellingham bridge on the North Tyne, and at this point it was presumably the largest since the bridge was completed in 1835. At Hexham construction of the Border Counties Railway bridge had just got under way when the scaffolding for the piers was carried away. It had reached a later stage (but was still described as a temporary viaduct) when it was struck again on 8 December and entirely carried away. In both cases there was flooding of the railway and houses in Derwenthaugh, Blaydon and Dunston.

Until the mid-1850s many riverside houses along the upper tidal reach were flooded with monotonous regularity. However, there was no comprehensive compilation of properties, and reporters with limited mobility described different locations. From the middle of the century, however, major works in the estuary, to improve navigation, also alleviated flooding.

THE ESTUARY IS TRANSFORMED
Until the mid-eighteenth century the river Tyne through Newcastle had quite a different appearance from that of today. Although the high tide reached beyond Newburn, the freshwater flow was the greatest influence on river level right down to Bill Point[22]. In this upper reach, the Tyne meandered in a shallow channel across the floodplain. The channel widened beyond Bill Point but large and shifting shoals and mudbanks were exposed at low water.

Although the banks at St Anthony's, Heworth and Hebburn 'continued to abound in pleasantness and rusticity' and trees and foliage bent down over the river at Bill Point, the river in its natural state was not compatible with the needs of shipping. The earliest authentic charts by Captain Collins in 1723 show the depth of water at the bar to be only seven feet at low water and twenty-one feet at high water. Fryer in 1800 reported that at low water there was not enough water to cross the river in a sculler. Rennie's survey in 1816 suggested a deterioration, with only six feet at the bar at low water and a minimum of four feet up to Newcastle. The inconvenience to shipping increased with the number, size and draught of vessels. By the 1850s larger ships waited for weeks unable to get back to sea laden, even at high water.

Responsibility for the management of the tidal river had been vested in the Corporation of Newcastle from the Middle Ages. However, they considered their responsibility was only to prevent it from getting worse rather than to make improvements. Little of the extensive revenues from shipping was put back into the river. The example of neighbouring Sunderland and its competition stimulated some interest after about 1840. In the first instance work was directed to the construction of river walls and jetties which, it was hoped, by confining the channel, would cause it to be self scouring. However, improvements were local and scouring in one place was often accompanied by deposition elsewhere.

There were persistent pleas from shipowners for more effective action and also calls from Gateshead and Shields for a role in river management. In 1850 the Tyne Improvement Act was passed. This transferred the responsibility for the conservation of the river to the Tyne Commissioners who had more equitable representation and, for the first time, they were obliged to use shipping dues to improve navigation. Even so, for another ten years the emphasis was on river training. It was not until after 1859, when the new engineer, Mr J.F. Ure, presented the case for dredging more forcefully in a report to the Commissioners, that uninterruped progress was made. Table 6.1 shows tonnages dredged in five-year periods.

Table 6.1 Quantities of material dredged from the Tyne and Northumberland Dock 1835-1990 (tons × 1000)

1835-40	78	1886-90	11542	1936-40	7644
1841-45	140	1891-95	8364	1941-45	6006
1846-50	275	1896-00	10099	1946-50	7136
1851-55	422	1901-05	10041	1951-55	7052
1856-60	1883	1906-10	9838	1956-60	5296
1861-65	13811	1911-15	9443	1961-65	5773
1866-70	22183	1916-20	5423	1966-70	5249
1871-75	15147	1921-25	8909	1971-75	1728
1876-80	9064	1926-30	6298	1976-80	3324
1881-85	14080	1931-35	6014	1981-85	3040
				1986-90	2201

Within twenty years the Tyne estuary was not only transformed for navigation but also (and largely incidentally) with respect to flooding. Guthrie[22] details some of the significant changes:
1. In 1860 the depth at the Bar was 6 feet 6 inches at low water and 21 feet 6 inches at high water springs; in 1879 it was at least 22 feet at low water and 37 feet at high water.
2. In 1860 at Newcastle Quayside, the foreshore in some places was 3 feet above low water and the greatest depth was 6 feet 6 inches; low water in 1879 varied from 10 to 20 feet.
3. Newcastle bridge, completed in 1781 after the failure of the medieval bridge in 1771, caused an obstruction to navigation as well as to river flow, with a significant difference between upstream and downstream water levels. In his report of 1859 Ure recommended its removal. The bridge was demolished in 1866 and the replacement swing bridge was completed in 1876.

4. Above the bridge deepening had progressed to Elswick and Dunston with a deepened channel on either side of King's Meadows Island. Low-water depths had increased from between 2 and 7 feet in 1860 to between 13 and 20 feet in 1879. In this reach prior to dredging there was a water surface slope of 2 feet per mile but in 1879 the low water surface was practically level as far as dredging had extended.

5. The river had been widened beyond Blaydon and the Lemington loop had been by-passed with a new channel cut through Blaydon Haugh.

6. In 1860 high tide at Newcastle and Newburn occurred respectively 60 and 90 minutes after high tide at Shields; by 1879, delay times had reduced to 12 and 20 minutes.

In the decade after 1879 dredging continued upstream to the tidal limit at Hedwin streams: the channel was straightened, widened and the banks protected. The narrow King's Meadows island, nearly half a mile in length, which lay off Elswick, with the smaller Annie and Little Annie islands, were acquired by the Tyne Commissioners and removed. Although uninhabited, King's Meadows was used for grazing sheep and cattle and during the early nineteenth century it was repeatedly reported covered during floods. Channel depth became greater upstream to Wylam, effectively extending the tidal limit, but this was partly a dynamic response of the river to greater downstream depth and partly due to gravel removal from the bed for building purposes: there was no navigational dredging above Hedwin Streams.

The overall effect of these changes was to make the tide the dominant control on water level throughout the estuary. The vastly increased estuary volume was able to absorb even the most extreme freshwater flow with little increase in level. Recent studies using a computer model show that with a repeat of the 1815 flood at Newburn, the level would not exceed 4.0 metres above Ordnance Datum, compared with the actual level of 7.5 metres above OD recorded on the flood stone at the Boathouse. There is not a single report of flooding from freshwater flow in the riverside villages below Newburn after 1856. Newcastle Quayside was covered for the last time on 8 February 1869. The focus of attention of floods shifted upstream beyond the tidal limit.

Dredging above the Newcastle bridges effectively ceased in the late 1960s and the reach has since been subject to natural siltation. The rate of accumulation is slow but, ultimately, perhaps after a century, one might expect a return to the flood vulnerability of the early nineteenth century.

A SCARCITY OF PARSLEY

The historic record shows remarkable variations from one period to another in the frequency and severity of flooding. Decades without an event of any significance may be followed by a period where severe floods occur in quick succession. After 1856 there were no exceptional floods for two decades. Those in January 1862, on 4 February 1868 and 8 February 1869 mainly affected agricultural land. But in 1875 a decade of severe incidents commenced which affected upland and lowland in both winter and summer, the most remarkable following the thaw of March 1881.

There is always the temptation to ascribe such flood eras (especially whilst still in them) to some change in land use within the catchment. The major change during the Victorian period was the growth of field drainage on a scale exceeding anything during the twentieth century. However, although drainage may have had some effect, its relationship to flooding is extraordinarily difficult to demonstrate, especially on catchments as large as the Tyne, because of the underlying variability in the occurrence of storm rainfall and snow.

In terms of average rainfall the period from 1875 to 1882 was wet, with six out of eight years with more than the long-term average. The period around the great flood of 1771 had also been wet nationally, with six out of eight years after 1768 above the average. My own view is that rainfall, not land use, was the primary control on the relative frequency of floods. Effects of heavy storm rainfall were amplified on catchments, wet from persistent rainfall and with high groundwater levels.

The first flood of this period centred on the lowlands on 14 November 1875 and, although the Tyne itself was not greatly affected, the Team was in heavy flood. At Beamish a mill race at a paper mill was swept away and a saw mill was badly damaged. Water lay three to four feet deep in the area now occupied by the Team Industrial Estate and, at nearby Lamesley, two boys were drowned in separate incidents.

In August 1877 after a summer which was said to be the wettest for fifty years, there was a flood on upland tributaries. At Allenheads, 140 mm of rain fell in July and 260 mm in August. A series of thunderstorms from 17 to 21 August especially affected the Nent and the South Tyne.

In the following year two floods had more widespread consequences. The first, on 21 January, occurred after prolonged rainfall and a south-westerly gale. At Hexham the water spread over Tyne Green and combined with the flow in Cockshaw and Cowgarth burns, to flood houses in Gilesgate knee-deep. The Tyne valley rail line was under water near Dilston and the tunnel at Farnley was blocked. At Ovingham there is the first report in the headmaster's log-book of flooding in the National School[23]. The school was built in 1871, presumably at a time when there was no immediate recollection of flooding at the site. It is situated adjacent to the Whittle burn, two hundred metres upstream from the confluence with the Tyne, and in high flows the water backs up the burn from the main river. The school log provides a comprehensive record of flooding through the period of the school's existence until it closed in 1969. (It is now the village scout hut.) On 21 January 1878, the depth in the school was four inches and pupils were given a holiday until their classroom dried out. The second flood, on the last day of 1878 following a thaw, was of lesser significance.

The winter of 1881 brought disruption and havoc to the Tyne as it did to the rest of northern Britain, with the period of deep snow continuing from early January until 9 March[24]. The cold was intense in mid-January with ice forming at the Quayside for the first time in twenty years. In early March, when improvement was expected, the worst snowstorm of the year struck. Railways and turnpikes alike were blocked with drifts up to twenty feet deep, even in lowland areas. Local trade came to a standstill and it was noted that the supply of vegetables to the market was curtailed and there was 'a particular scarcity of parsley'. The General Soup Kitchen was reopened in the Manors.

A slow thaw set in on 6 March. It became rapid on the 9th, when the wind veered west and river levels rose steadily through the day reaching a peak at Hexham at 11 p.m. The dam at Fourstones paper mill on the South Tyne was badly damaged and water was seven feet deep over its crest. At Hexham, houses and lanes around Tyne Mills were flooded and waters spread out over the Nursery Grounds at Hollow Orchard and Robson's Bankfoot Nurseries. The *Hexham Courant* reported that by nightfall the stone arches of the Border Counties railway bridge were choking full and the water was within three feet of the iron spans in the centre. Inhabitants recalled the flood of 1856 when the bridge at the site was swept away and reckoned that the level was then two-and-a-half feet higher.

At Ovingham the schoolroom was overflowed to a depth of eight inches and at Wylam the Tyne also overtopped its banks. Several waterside houses were flooded and 'inmates had to fly to their garrets for safety'. George Stephenson's birthplace was 'entirely flooded out'. Water covered a large area from Close House to Newburn Treatment Works and, on the Scotswood, Newburn and Wylam railway, ballast was washed from beneath the sleepers.

The alleviating effects of dredging had not yet progressed to this upper reach of the estuary but, with the changes over the following decades, the chance of a recurrence rapidly diminished. Opposite Stephenson's cottage the riverside footpath follows a low degraded floodbank which now stands well proud of the highest floods.

Two large floods followed in 1883 and 1886. The first on 29 January 1883 was again caused by heavy rain on melting snow which had lain for only two days. At Hexham, the North British Railway bridge seemed endangered by large trees lodged against the piers. It was deemed safer for the passengers to walk across the bridge, the train following slowly behind and taking them up at the other end. At Tyne Green, water came up to the doors of cottages close to the wall of Spital Park and at Corbridge fields between the station and the Tunnel (now the grounds of Tynedale Rugby Club) were three feet deep in water. One observer at Hexham stated the flood was greater than in 1881 but this is unlikely as the water did not enter the Ovingham School house. However, the school was closed, 'children being unable to reach it on account of the floods'. The flood of 6 November 1886 was less serious except on the Team where 90 mm of rain fell in two days and houses were flooded to a depth of three or four feet.

The frequency of flooding diminished again from 1886 until the end of the century, the only flood of note being on 2 September 1892 when the children of Ovingham were again given a free day as the school was surrounded by water.

OUSEBURN AND TEAM IN TURMOIL
The Ouseburn and the Team are the main tributaries draining urban Tyneside.

Before 1900 flooding on the Ouseburn was virtually unknown. On the Team, floods generally attracted less attention than on the main Tyne although there had been serious floods there in 1828, 1841, 1852, 1875 and 1886. The storms of 1900 and 1903 gave Tynesiders a different perspective on their peaceful native streams.

On Friday 26 October a light shower of snow was a prelude to a night of driving rain which became heavier as the night progressed and continued until noon on Saturday with a north to north westerly gale. By 9 a.m. on the 27th most raingauges on Tyneside had recorded over 75 mm with the highest total of 93mm at Jesmond. So chilling was the rain that several people died of exposure within sight of their homes. Because of inadequate urban drainage, road and rail traffic were disrupted and numerous homes flooded. At North Bank, Howdon, a woman pensioner was drowned in her own home with ten feet of water in her kitchen. Other occupants escaped through the roof.

In the rural upper reaches of the Ouseburn a hundred sheep perished at Brunton Farm and another fifty at Middle Brunton. At Low Gosforth an old couple, who had lived in their cottage for more than sixty years, declined rescue although the water was up to the level of their bedstead. But nearby, in Ash Street, an invalid was carried out as the water reached her mattress.

The burn through Jesmond Dene was 'a rushing roaring torrent' but was held back and formed a pond behind Benton Bridge. From the Armstrong bridge just upstream there was a view of the flooded farm below, with the occupants gazing forlornly from the upper floor whilst their poultry houses and livestock were carried off. At the foot of Ouseburn Road, the burn overflowed and occupants in Crawford Road and Bryson Terrace had to escape by their back doors[25].

Along the Team the scene was 'like a continuous lake on which a barge might have navigated from Birtley to Dunston'. The main rail line was impassable. The intrepid reporter sent to record the incident seems not to have got further than the tram terminus at the Magpie Inn on the corner of Ropery and Derwentwater roads. From the upstairs window he could see the lake extending round Carnaby Terrace to the south, covering Eslington Park and continuing along the main road to Dunston. A large part of the Gateshead Garden Festival site was under water. Across the lake the Eslington Arms and Amie Terrace were inundated. Towards the Tyne a cement factory and a sawmill were surrounded, the only evidence of the latter being a red tiled roof and floating timber. Kiln fires at Lucas Fire Brickworks were extinguished and more than ten thousand bricks were destroyed.

Three years later there was a remarkable repetition of Ouse and Team flooding but on this occasion the rainfall was more widespread. Over northern England, October 1903 was the wettest on record with most sites in Northumbria recording more than 200mm in the month. In Newcastle over the two-day period 8 to 9 October, 103mm fell – more than in 1900 but over a longer period. The flood was marginally less serious on the Ouseburn but much more severe on the Team where a hundred families were affected. In the Magpie Inn the water was up to the bar. At Dunston and Norwood collieries the fan engines were stopped by an inrush of water. Dozens of houses were flooded in Paper Mill Square and Carnaby Terrace as well as a Wesleyan chapel and school.

Since that date no floods have remotely approached these two in magnitude. There were lesser floods which affected the Team on 1 June 1924, 18 December 1968 and 29 March 1979. By the time of the last two, most of the residential property affected in the earlier floods had been removed and, above High Teams bridge, the river had been straight-jacketed in an open concrete flume through the Trading Estate and was no longer a serious danger. Downstream from High Teams the river is tidal and was dredged by the Port of Tyne Authority until 1963. After that date siltation added to the problems where industrial properties, including the ropeworks, remained vulnerable to the combined effects of flood and high tide. Channel works carried out in that reach in 1981 now provide protection against all but the most extreme events26.

Houses affected along the Ouseburn in 1900 have also gone. Bryson Terrace lasted only until 1906 when the burn was placed in a massive concrete culvert from Jesmond Vale to below Byker Bridge, covered over and topped with the City Stadium. No doubt the massive dimensions of the culvert were a reflection of the flood volume in 1900, but it proved a life saver to many during World War II when it was used as a bomb shelter. The main concern now on the Ouseburn is for the effects of increasing urbanisation (already over fifty percent of the catchment) on the speed and volume of runoff. Flood storage ponds may be necessary to counteract these changes.

MORE FLOOD STONES

On the main Tyne the October flood of 1903 reached its peak on the morning of the 7th, two days earlier than on its urban tributaries. It was the largest since 1881, flooding a number of houses at Hexham including Kingshaw Green, the Spital Lodge (eighteen inches deep) and others on Tyne Green. The infant's room at Ovingham School was covered to a depth of three inches and, after a lull on the 8th, the water rose again and surrounded the building on the 9th.

At Bywell the water swirled around the old market cross and in front of Bywell House, where the level is marked on another set of flood stones, recording four events of the twentieth century. The engraved dates and surveyed levels (above Ordnance Datum) are as follows:

January   1903   18.29m OD
October   1925   18.64m
April   1947   18.48m
January   1955   18.98m

By comparison, the 1771 flood level (exaggerated by the weir) has been estimated at 22.25m at St Peter's church. It is interesting that the months of occurrence in 1903 and 1925 have been transposed – a strong indication that the stones were etched long after both events. The precision of the recorded levels is therefore doubtful.

The two decades after 1903 were remarkably flood free on the Tyne, as on the other main rivers in Northumbria, although headwater tributaries did not entirely escape. It was not until the mid-1920s that the river again began to

Plate 6.12 The Ouseburn in Jesmond Vale during the flood of 9 October 1903. Residents in the cottage in the foreground were rescued by horse and carts. *Photo. J. Blacklock.*

excite the interest of local reporters and photographers. On several occasions in the 1920s and 1930s, the water crept out over the floodplain and on to roads but rarely penetrated houses. The biggest of these floods appear to have been those of New Year 1925, as recorded at Bywell, and 20 September 1926, the date engraved on a flood stone at Hermitage Mill, Hexham.

There were further floods on 21 September 1927 and 16 November 1929 (both mainly on the South Tyne) and on 1 February 1933, a mainly North Tyne flood after a thaw. The level at Bellingham was just two feet below the 1856 engraved flood mark on the bridge and two houses were flooded in the nearby square.

During the war the heavy snows of February 1941 were followed by a snowmelt flood on the seventeenth which escaped report in the papers but was recorded in the Headmaster's report at Ovingham where the school was surrounded but not entered. The long winter of 1947 ended on 22 April with a flood of similar magnitude to that of 1941. The recently formed Northumberland and Tyne River Board reported serious damage to flood banks and flooding of haughs below Hexham from Beaufront to Dilston. Houses were flooded at Warden, Hexham and Corbridge. On the South Tyne flood waters reached the door of Riverside House, Haydon Bridge, and lay three feet deep on the Warden to Fourstones road.

The floods of the winter 1954-5 showed the continued susceptibility of riverside roads and dwellings to the river's vagaries. So far as I am aware, these were the last events to have had their levels engraved in stone. In 1988 Bill Robson still farmed at Hesleyside Mill above Bellingham, where he had lived since 1934. He recalled how, after the flood of 2 December 1954, he had engraved the remarkable level on the stone door frame of a barn, only to see the river rise an inch higher on 10 January 1955. Thus the two largest floods of the century on the North Tyne were separated by little more than a month. In addition to the flood mark at Bywell the January 1955 level is also recorded (twice) by engraving on the wall of the old pumping station near Wylam.

THE GREATEST OF THE TWENTIETH CENTURY (1954 AND 1955)
The autumn of 1954 was exceedingly wet, and during October there were three floods of sufficient magnitude to excite the interest of the local press, on 3, 18 and 29. The flood of 18 October was the largest of these and had its main source on the South Tyne. A bakery was flooded at Haltwhistle, and at Warden a bungalow (Linden Lea) was surrounded and firemen waded shoulder-high to carry children to safety. On the main Tyne the level was only three inches below the 1947 flood level at Prudhoe and the pumphouse at the ICI works only just escaped. As if in warning of things to come, the floodwaters reached the wall of the maternity hospital (now The Lion of Corbridge Hotel) at the south end of the bridge at Corbridge.

It was the turn of the North Tyne on 2 December, when the river spread out over the haugh land above Bellingham. At Tarset, children rode on horseback from their school at Greystead, with water up to the stirrups in places. Low Eals farm at Tarset was flooded knee-deep. At Bellingham, houses at Brookside Place and Fallowfield were flooded. Cattle and poultry were washed down river and a haystack was seen in the current with three otters perched on top. At Corbridge the Tyne edged a little higher than in October and into the maternity hospital. Firemen were called to pump it out.

At the turn of the year, with the ground thoroughly saturated from these earlier floods, snow began to accumulate in the upper parts of the catchment, accompanied by an intense frost. There was only a two-day break in winter's icy grip, but the thaw accompanied by rain on a frozen catchment was sufficient to produce the biggest flood on the Tyne since 1815. Rainfall totals averaging 50 mm were not exceptional by upland standards and the highest two-day rainfalls were 66 mm at Whickhope (North Tyne) and 68.3 mm at Alston. However, the flood of 10 January 1955 was unusual in that the peaks at the confluence of North and South Tyne coincided, with a resulting increase in severity downstream.

On the North Tyne there was a repeat performance of the December flood with haugh land and roads flooded. At Bellingham a resident recalled watching at the bridge as the level rose well above the engraved mark of 1856. On the river Rede houses were flooded in West Woodburn and others abandoned at Hindhaugh. At Humshaugh the mill was five feet and the mill house one foot under water.

The main centre of action on the South Tyne was at Warden which was still unprotected by flood banks. In the morning of Monday 10, villagers woke early

to find the river already in spate, and it rose another ten feet in four hours. By
11 a.m., the Boatside Inn was flooded to a depth of two to three feet and,
outside, the water ran level with the top of the garden wall. At nearby cottages
the water had risen to the top of ground floor windows. Two residents
attempted to escape by crawling along a builder's ladder from a bedroom
window to the parapet of Warden bridge and, with the others, were eventually
rescued by the Fire Brigade. Families were also trapped in houses at West Boat.
Twenty-one houses were flooded. The level was three feet six inches in the
primary school and the Methodist Chapel was flooded. The church hall was
invaded as the vicar's wife was setting up a centre for evacuees. At nearby
Fourstones, the water was four feet deep in the paper mill and the Tyne Metal
Foundry.

Downstream at Hexham, the whole of Tyne Green was under water and at
Pickering's timber yard (now a caravan site), the timber was cast adrift. Spital
Cottage and Nursery Cottage were flooded. On the North bank Miss Bettine
Morant at the Hermitage indicated the maximum level on the drive adjacent to
the raised 1771 and 1815 flood marks. Comparative surveyed levels are:

1771   37.15m OD
1815   36.39m OD
1955   35.79m OD

Floodbanks between Corbridge and Hexham were breached or overtopped
and, south of the river at Corbridge, the water spilled out over a wide area
between the bridge and the railway station. Mothers and babies were evacuated
from the maternity hospital. Residents at Station Road, including the Station
Hotel, were confined to their bedrooms for nearly twelve hours as the water
reached a maximum of over four feet on the ground floor (Plate 6.13).
Seventeen homes were flooded. An impatient motorist attempting to approach
the bridge was halted as part of the parapet fell and water flowed past his car
like a mill race. He found refuge on a garden wall but was trapped waist deep
for over an hour. A lorry containing a rowing boat was backed to the water's
edge and the boat, secured by a rope, was launched towards the marooned man
who finally managed to scramble aboard and be dragged shivering to safety.

At Ovingham the village primary school had just reopened for the new term.
The careful hand of the Headmaster, Bob Walker, records in the log[23]:

At 11.45 the burn beside the school became so badly flooded that water was up to the
top step of the infants' cloakroom. As an emergency measure, I informed pupils they
should report for school as usual tomorrow and dismissed the school. We could only
leave via Jordan's field and private gardens. School dinner van reached Bridge End Inn
and was turned back with dinners unused.

In fact the school did not resume again for a week. The water at its peak had
risen to twenty-one inches in the infants' room and fifteen inches in the large
room. The stock of books was largely ruined and Mr Walker, who still (1992)
lives nearby, reports wryly that the flood did more to procure new books and
equipment than years of begging letters to the Education Office. Across the

Plate 6.13 Station Road, Corbridge during the flood of 10 January 1955. *Photo*. Evening Chronicle.

Plate 6.14 The army help to repair the breached floodbank upstream from the bridge at Corbridge after the flood of 10 January 1955. *Photo*. Evening Chronicle.

river at Prudhoe the Blaydon store cornershop was awash and in nearby Tyne House the water was one foot deep. The pump house at ICI and other parts of the works were flooded.

The 1955 flood sparked off activity all along the river. The army were called in for emergency repair of breached floodbanks, (Plate 6.14), and 150 servicemen worked in exacting conditions as winter resumed its grasp. Flooded fields became ice-rinks as temperatures fell next day to –8°C.

Reinstatement of banks continued through the summer, costing the River Board £18,600. New banks and floodwalls were designed and built at Warden and Corbridge, with the intention of providing protection to a level one foot above the January flood[27]. Bridges at Warden and Corbridge were modified to increase their flood capacity. Islands in the river North Tyne above and below the bridge at Bellingham, which had impeded the flow, were removed. A flood warning scheme, based on level alarm gauges at Haltwhistle and Bellingham, was initiated by the River Board and the first gauging station on the Tyne capable of monitoring flood flows was built at Bywell in 1956.

THE ERA OF RECORDS

Since 1955, scientific monitoring of the river has much improved, with many more gauging stations and the latest in electronic communications equipment. The flood warning system, now under the control of the National Rivers Authority, is primed for action. There has been nothing yet to match the flood of 1955 but a number of lesser floods are readily recalled by riverside villagers.

Floods of 17 October 1967 and 23 March 1968 were approximately equal on the river Tyne and the highest since measured records began (Plate 6.15). Much agricultural land was flooded and many roads were impassable including the A69 at Greenhead, Bardon Mill and Corbridge. However, the floodbanks prevented a repeat of flooding of houses at Warden and Corbridge and flood warning enabled farmers to move stock to safety[28]. In October the most serious problems were at Greenhead where the Tipalt Burn overflowed and flooded the school and several houses.

The flood of 30 August 1975, at the end of a dry summer, was centred on the North Tyne where up to 88mm of rain fell in nine hours[29]. It is principally remembered for its disastrous effect on Bellingham Show, as access to it was largely cut off. Up river at Lewisburn, three families of workers at the Kielder dam site were made homeless as their caravans were washed away.

Floods on the South Tyne in December 1979 exposed one weak spot in the protective works – at Warden where a riverside bungalow was flooded at Coastley Burnfoot. The house was flooded five more times, the last and worst to one metre depth on 26 August 1986, just a few days before work was due to start on a mini–floodbank (Plate 6.16). Although there is still occasional flooding of roads and agricultural land, flooding of buildings has been eliminated in all but the most extreme floods.

Plate 6.16 Coastly Burnfoot, Warden, during the flood of 26 August 1986.
Photo. Evening Chronicle.

FOREST AND RESERVOIR

The South Tyne catchment remains in a comparatively natural state with respect to its hydrology. However, two major changes in the land use of the North Tyne have radically affected flood flows: afforestation and reservoir construction. The effect of forests on the quantity and quality of rivers has long been a source of argument between foresters and river users, and results from scientific experiments seemed to conflict. A report in 1948 by the Central Advisory Water Committee[30] concluded that:

The major beneficial effects of forest in gathering grounds are the prevention of erosion and the regulation of streamflow by the absorption of water from sudden heavy rain and its comparatively slow release by percolation.

The first blow to this notion of forested catchments having greater runoff, and being less flashy and less erosive, came in the mid-1950s when experiments in Lancashire showed reduced runoff from mature forest[31]. These results were confirmed by intensive studies comparing forested and moorland catchments in mid–Wales, which also showed the forested catchments carried more sediment, though they tended to have lower flood discharges[32]. The latter is not invariably the case, as experiments on a small catchment at Coal Burn, just over the border in Cumbria, demonstrated. Flood peaks there on a newly forested catchment were forty percent higher than they had been on undisturbed moorland[33].

The age of the forest is the most critical factor in flood flows. Before trees can be established on the wet moorland soils, a suitably aerated environment for rooting must be created. To achieve this, it has been the practice to dig deep drainage ditches up and down slopes. Drains are typically half-a-metre deep at about five-metre spacing, giving a length of two hundred kilometres for every square kilometre. The trees are planted on the sod thrown out at the side of the drain.

It is these drains, rather than the trees themselves, which are the main influence on the flood response of afforested land during the early years of growth. Storm rainfall and surface flow are much more quickly and efficiently transported to the main channel, giving a more flashy response with higher flood peaks.

In contrast, mature trees tend to reduce flood runoff, especially when the conifer canopy closes. The trees intercept rainfall and return more of it to the atmosphere as evaporation; the soil below becomes drier and retains more moisture at the onset of a flood. Ultimately this effect becomes more important and flood peaks (certainly in small to moderate floods) diminish to less than those on the adjacent moorland. But how soon does this happen? The answer is uncertain but the canopy closes in something between ten and twenty years, and it is probably in this period that the flood response switches from drain dominance to canopy dominance.

It is interesting to follow the progress of afforestation at Kielder (Fig 6.3). Although planting began in the late 1920s, it was only after World War II that developments progressed at a grand scale with mechanisation of drainage. The highest annual acreages were planted in the early 1950s but by the mid-1960s mature forest began to predominate. It is tempting to ascribe the two most severe floods of the century on the North Tyne, in December 1954 and January 1955, to the extensive forest drainage, but it must be remembered that there were massive floods at the same time on the South Tyne with its moorland headwaters. One can at least be certain that the newly planted forest made the North Tyne catchment more vulnerable to storm rainfall.

Whilst the role of the forest in flooding remains fundamental for upland tributaries, the effect on the main river has been dwarfed by the even greater impact of Kielder Water, completed in 1980, which exerts a distinct but diminishing effect right through to the Tyne estuary.

An area of 240 square kilometres, mostly forested, drains into Kielder Water and the dam above Falstone holds back a volume of nearly two hundred million cubic metres (two hundred million tonnes). Releases are made from this storage in a pattern quite different from the natural flow[34] and an important effect is the reduction in flood flows downstream. Storage in the reservoir, even when it is full and spilling, reduces the peak flow downstream to less than half of what would naturally have occurred. In addition, the operating policy for hydropower is designed to keep the reservoir drawn down below the full level to ensure that as much of the stored water as possible can be put through the turbines to generate power and revenue. Floods upstream are largely captured

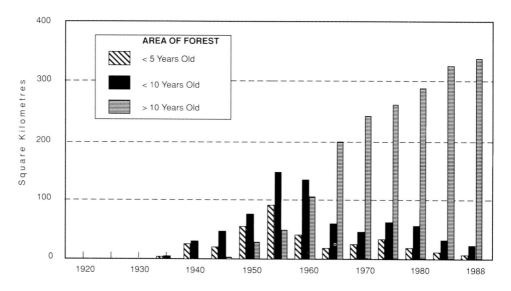

Fig 6.3 Progress of afforestation at Kielder showing most rapid growth during the 1950s.

and serve only to raise the reservoir level.

Figure 6.4 contrasts the scale of changes in river level measured at Tarset, eight kilometres downstream from the reservoir. The flood of 30 August 1975 caused a rise in level of 3.6 metres in contrast to the mere 0.4 metres resulting from the switching on of the turbines, and a maximum of 1.1 metres with all the valves open. Nevertheless, there remains concern at the rate of rise in level from low flow, and Northumbrian Water have agreed to build up the level over a two-hour period so that the rise does not exceed 0.19 metres (7.5 inches) in fifteen minutes.

Further downstream where tributary inflows are unaffected especially below the South Tyne confluence, the effects of Kielder Water diminish. At the tidal limit the Kielder catchment represents only about one tenth of the total catchment area. The existence of Kielder has therefore by no means eliminated the possibility of flooding in this downstream reach.

THE PLEASURES OF TYNE

It would be inappropriate in a valley with such beauty of changing scene and season as the Tyne to begin and end with the horrors of flooding. I will leave it to the poet Akenside, from his *Pleasures of Imagination*, to give redress.

O ye dales
Of Tyne, and ye most ancient woodlands, where
Oft as the giant flood obliquely strides,
And his banks open, and his lawns extend,
Stops short the pleased traveller to view
Presiding o'er the scene some rustic tower
Founded by Norman or by Saxon hands.

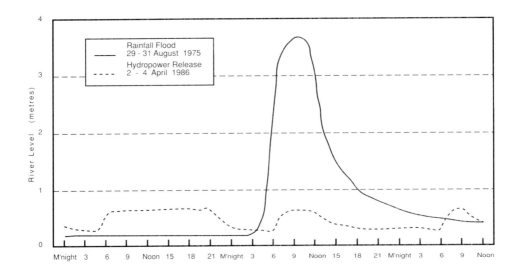

Fig 6.4 Comparison of the effects of a natural flood and a hydropower release from Kielder on downstream water levels (at Tarset).

REFERENCES

1. Machine Letters vol. 2, Austhorpe 27 Oct 1783. Letter from Smeaton to Errington.
2. Smith, D. 'The professional correspondence of John Smeaton, an eighteenth century consulting engineering practice', *Trans. Newcomen Soc.* vol. 47 (1974-76)
3. Natural Environment Research Council, *United Kingdom Yearbook of Hydrological Data*, (1990)
4. Maxwell, H. *Chronicle of Lanercost 1272-1346* (2 vols, 1913)
5. Stow, J. *Annales, or a General Chronicle of England*, (1580) Continued to 1614 by E. Howes, (London, 1615)
6. Brand, J. *History and Antiquities of the Town and County of the Town of Newcastle upon Tyne*, (2 vols, London, 1789)
7. Northumberland County. Quarter Sessions Order Books
8. Garrett, W. *Account of Floods in 1815 and 1771*
9. Anon. Record of the Charity established for sufferers from the Great Flood of 1771 in the County of Northumberland. Northumberland Record Office.
10. Wallace, J. *The Natural History and Antiquities of Northumberland and North Durham*, (London, 1769)
11. Graham, F. *The Bridges of Northumberland and Durham*, Newcastle upon Tyne (1975) (showing an illustration of Bywell by Thomas Allom, dated 1834)
12. Bell, J. *Account of floods in 1815 and 1771*
13. Horsley, P.M. *Eighteenth Century Newcastle*, especially Chapter 1, 'Tyne Bridge', (Newcastle upon Tyne, 1971)
14. Ruddock, E. C. 'The foundations of Hexham Bridge', *Geotechnique*, vol. 27, no 3, (1977)
15. Sykes, J. A collection of publications relating to Newcastle upon Tyne, including a 'Biographical note of the late John Gibson of Sandhoe'. Tract, (1821)
16. Gotch, C. 'Robert Mylne and Tyne bridges'. *Archaeologia Aeliana*, Fourth Series. 33, Society of Antiquaries, Newcastle upon Tyne, (1955)
17. Maclean, J. S. *The Newcastle and Carlisle Railway*, (1948)

18. Northumberland County Record Office. County Surveyor Misc. 15/6 (1832-7)
19. Ibid. 43 (1880)
20. Johnson, Revd. A. Handwritten notes in the Parish Register of Bywell St Peter. NCRO 2441
21. Richardson, M. A. *Memorials of Floods*
22. Guthrie, J. *The River Tyne, its History and Resources*, (London, 1880)
23. Ovingham National School Headmasters' Log Books, NCRO, (1870-1969)
24. Duncan, W. Unpublished Local Records
25. Ellison, E. L. Memories of Jesmond Vale. (compiled by Cara Sanderson), (Newcastle upon Tyne, 1980)
26. Northumbrian River Authority 'River Team Flood Relief Scheme', Engineer's Report.
27. Northumberland and Tyneside River Board. Annual Reports (1951-65)
28. Northumbrian River Authority, 'River Tyne, Reconstruction of Floodbanks between Hexham and Corbridge', Engineer's Report (1970)
29. Northumbrian Water Authority 'Flooding on the River Tyne, 30 August 1975', Minutes of Regional Land Drainage Committee (Oct. 1975)
30. Ministry of Health. *Gathering grounds. Public access to gathering grounds, afforestation and agriculture on gathering grounds*, Central Water Advisory Committee, (London, 1948)
31. Law, F 'The effect of afforestation upon the water yield of catchment areas', *Journal of the British Waterworks Assn.* 38 (1956)
32. Institute of Hydrology 'Water balance of headwater catchments of the Wye and Severn, 1970-75', *Institute of Hydrology Report* 33 (1976)
33. Robinson, M. 'The effect of pre-afforestation drainage on the streamflow and water quality of a small upland catchment', *Institute of Hydrology, Report* 73 (1980)
34. Johnson, P. 'River regulation: a regional perspective – Northumbria Water Authority', *Regulated Rivers: Research and Management* 2 (1988)

7. RIVERS WANSBECK AND BLYTH

O ye Northumbrian shades which overlook
The rocky pavement and the mossy falls
of solitary Wensbeck's limpid stream
Akenside Pleasures of Imagination

The Wansbeck and Blyth are in many respects similar rivers (Table 7.1). They ·
drain lowland catchments of the same area and both rise to the east of the Tyne
and are cradled between the Tyne and the coast.

Both catchments lie almost entirely on rocks of Carboniferous age, with the
Fell Sandstone in the northern headwaters of the Wansbeck giving the highest
crags at Tosson. Millstone Grit underlies the middle reaches whilst Coal
Measures extend from Morpeth to the coast. The hard rocks of the Whin Sill
form low crags near Kirkwhelpington. Both catchments have predominantly
undulating farmland but there is also a significant area of rough pasture in the
headwaters of the Wansbeck, stretching from Sweethope Loughs through
Kirkwhelpington Common to Tosson Hill at the western end of the Simonside
Hills (Figure 7.1). About thirty square kilometres of this higher land has been
afforested.

Table 7.1 Comparative catchment statistics for Wansbeck and Blyth:

	Wansbeck	Blyth
Catchment area	339.4 km²	339.4km²
Land above 200 metres OD	110.0 km²	13.7km²
% above 200 metres OD	32.4%	4.0%
Highest point	440 m OD	268 m OD
Channel slope	6.9 m/km	4.9 m/km
Mean annual rainfall	839 mm	726 mm

In one significant way the rivers differ. There is remarkably little flooding
along the river Blyth, although the storm of 1 April 1992 showed the continuing
vulnerability of houses in Ponteland from its tributary, the river Pont. The
Wansbeck in contrast has the doubtful distinction amongst Northumbrian rivers
of having had the most damaging flood of the twentieth century. This was the
flood of March 1963, of which more later.

WANSBECK AND MORPETH

The lower Wansbeck flows in an incised and wooded channel and, with the
exception of the old mill at Bothal and a few houses at Sheepwash, now
demolished, all buildings have been above the reach of the river. Above

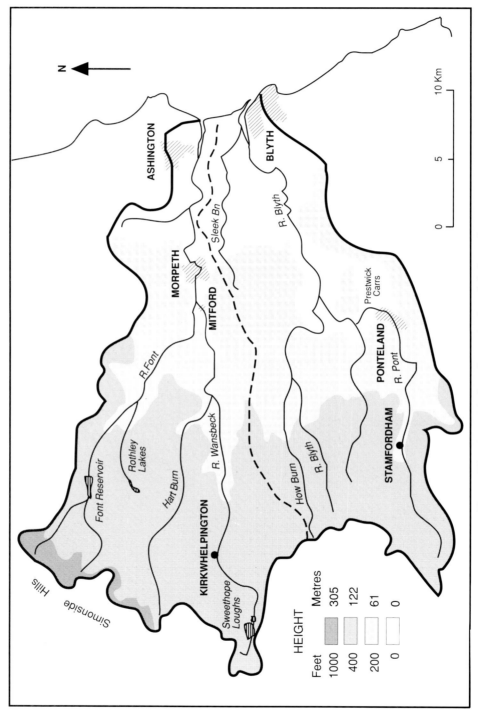

Fig 7.1 The rivers Blyth and Wansbeck and their catchments.

Morpeth, there are no vulnerable properties on either the Wansbeck or on its principal tributaries the Hart burn and the river Font.

It is quite a different story in Morpeth. It is situated on a broad loop of the Wansbeck, with part of the town built on the river's natural floodplain (Fig 7.2). Naturally it has had to bear the consequences. The flooded areas have extended from Mitford Road upstream to Low Stanners downstream. Affected locations include parts of the High Stanners, a riverside strip from the New Market to Oliver's Mill, a broad area stretching from the Telford Bridge to the mouth of the Cotting burn and, on the opposite bank, Goose Hill and Bennett's Walk. Hodgson[1], in 1832, surmised that the name 'stanners' derived from the gravel heaps deposited by floods and their vulnerability is therefore not surprising.

Seven bridges cross the river through the town, four pedestrian and three road bridges. Although bridges have occasionally been overtopped, they have not fared as badly as on flashier rivers further south. With one early exception velocities have been insufficient to destroy the town's road bridges.

Three small tributary burns thread their way through the town and, although normally insignificant, they have caused problems through flash floods generated on their own catchments or by backing up from the Wansbeck. The Cotting burn (also known in its lower course as the Tanner's burn from the industries which lined its banks until the end of the last century[2]) approaches the town from the north-east and flows down the back of Newgate Street. It is culverted below Copper Chare and Dacre Street, periodically emerging and finally turning sharply northward to join the Wansbeck. The lowest reach of the Cotting burn from a very early date (shown on the first town map of 1604) formed part of the mill race which ran from the Chantry to power three mills, the manorial mill on the site of Saint George's church until 1860, the Dob (or bleaching) mill, and a waulk (or fulling) mill at the confluence with the Wansbeck. The head of water to drive these mills was provided by a weir which ran diagonally across the river at the site of the Telford bridge. This may have exacerbated flooding upstream until its removal in 1832. On the south bank, the Church burn and its tributary the Postern burn, and the Allery burn join the main river at opposite ends of Bennett's Walk.

The Wansbeck itself becomes little more than a trickle during prolonged dry summers. In 1989 the flow fell as low as 0.12 cubic metres per second and the modest public water supply abstraction at Mitford, two kilometres upstream, had to stop for four months. The river's agricultural catchment responds slowly to rainfall and it is usually only after lengthy winter rainfall or a thaw that it changes its character. In the past, long periods of quiescence encouraged building at low levels adjacent to the river.

EARLY FLOODS

Given the extent of damage in later floods, the records of early floods in Morpeth seem surprisingly sparse. This is no doubt due to the location of early settlement away from the river. It is recorded that a stone bridge leading to the Abbey of Newminster, and probably at the site of the Lowford bridge, was destroyed in a flood of 1609. The quarter sessions[3] held in 1680 ordered that

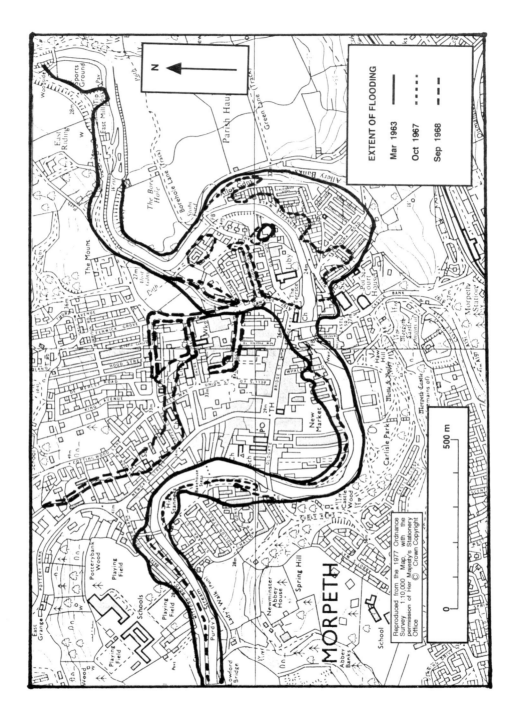

Fig 7.2 Morpeth in a double loop of the river Wansbeck has suffered both from the main river and its small tributary the Cotting burn.

'care be taken to preserve the remaining stones of the Abbey Bridge, most of them being gone already'.

The next record dates from 6 October 1739 when the *Newcastle Journal* reported that 'the river at Morpeth which is otherwise a small one swelled above what has been known and did considerable damage'. A large piece of the mill dam near Morpeth's medieval bridge was carried away. At the warp mill (almost certainly the waulk mill) water ran over the top of the door, and corn, trees, calves, sheep and hogs were borne down the river.

There are no further reports until 9 November 1761 when Hodgson notes that the arches of the bridge were nearly filled and that overflowing water ran down Oldgate and Bridge Street to the east end of the town. This implies a very severe flood or changes in local topography for, even in the great flood of 1963, the water at these two sites was not connected, and flooding at the east end of Bridge Street arose from water overflowing the banks in the immediate vicinity.

The Wansbeck and Morpeth appear to have escaped entirely the devastation of floods to north and south in 1770 and 1771. This independence of response has been shown by later floods to be by no means unusual. However, the snowmelt flood of 10 March 1782 which wrought such havoc to the bridges of the Tyne also caused some alarm at Morpeth when the river rose twelve feet above its usual level at the north arch of the old bridge and 'all low grounds adjoining Morpeth overflowed'.

TELFORD BRIDGE AND FLOOD RECORDS
After a gap of more than thirty years, five floods were recorded in only four years, perhaps, at least in part, because of their significance for the construction of Morpeth's new bridge.

The town's medieval bridge was probably built in the late thirteenth century. The roadway was only eleven and a half feet wide, steeply humpbacked and a hazard to coaches, two of which had fallen into the river in the 1820s.

A new bridge was sanctioned by Act of Parliament. Designs were submitted by John Dobson and by Thomas Telford and, in spite of Hodgson's claim that Dobson was the designer, it was Telford's three-arch plan that was selected. Indeed, the bridge bears a hallmark of Telford's design in the bevelled *corne de vache* entry to the arches, a feature which he had previously used in his Severn bridge at Gloucester, and which, whilst aesthetically pleasing, has an engineering function in giving smoother entry and increased capacity in flood flows. Dobson can claim responsibility only for the temporary quarry bridge which had spanned at the same point for a decade, and was used for carrying stone for the building of the gaol.

Bridge building commenced in 1829 but in the previous year two floods were recorded on 13 July and 1 December. In the latter report, the *Newcastle Chronicle* noted that 'the flood almost touched the chain bridge' which had been erected just two years earlier at the site of the present Oldgate Bridge[4]. These floods no doubt gave a good indication of the river's flood potential and of the required height and capacity of the bridge. Two further floods occurred during construction, on 17 October 1829 and 9 February 1831, and, although the latter was 'higher than it was ever known before', there is no record that it had any impact on the new bridge.

The bridge had one further early test of its strength and stability on 15 September 1839, when the river reached a level which ranks with 1898 and 1963 amongst the highest in the historic period. It was a flood which affected rivers northward to the Tweed, following continuous heavy rain through the previous day. A dam at Netherwitton was destroyed. At Morpeth the water rose (variously) two or three feet higher than 'the great flood of February 1831' and the water was several feet deep in some houses at Morpeth. A wooden bridge at Morpeth quarry was destroyed and at the East Mill the water nearly reached the first storey. A stack of hay was taken from Bothal Haughs, carried out to sea about four miles and finally landed quite whole on Newbiggin Sand. In some houses at Sheepwash the water got into the second storey. 'There was never a flood in this river which caused so much damage, but no lives lost.'

VICTORIAN URBAN DEVELOPMENT AND FLOODING

An 1826 map of Morpeth shows that up to that time the inhabitants had largely avoided building on lower areas adjacent to the river. There were just three or four houses on the High Stanners opposite the Bakehouse steps (Charleton Cottages), and the area from Telford bridge to Low Stanners was largely vacant. The Cottage stood alone on the south bank opposite Bennett's field. By the end of the nineteenth century, however, all these areas had seen the development of housing and, in some places, industries had also been established.

Maps of 1860 and 1897 show the progress of development. Although High Stanners was virtually unchanged between 1826 and 1860, by 1897 there were a dozen houses more in Abbey View and Terrace in addition to the stone building which now houses Morpeth social club[5]. On the Low Stanners a group of thirteen houses was built before 1860 and the gasworks were established on slightly higher ground in 1832. Beechfield House and buildings at the Willows were constructed before 1860 and nearby, at Damside, there were new industries, including the timber yard and saw mill on a site near the present roundabout, at the junction of Gas Works Lane and Damside. Individual houses and small terraces sprang up along Bennett's Walk: Wansbeck Terrace and Laurel House before 1860 and Melbourne Terrace before 1897. Tenter Terrace was erected in 1875 and at Goosehill the number of houses grew from six to sixteen between 1860 and 1897.

It is interesting that building continued on the floodplain in the late Victorian era in a period of severe and persistent flooding. Between 1863 and 1903 there were twelve occasions when buildings in Morpeth were flooded. Table 7.2 summarises occurrences reported in the local press.

In the flood of 1863 on 11 June the river rose to its highest level since 1839. Roadways in parts of Bennett's Walk and Captain Brummell's garden and The Terrace gardens below Telford bridge were under water. The Prince Albert Inn, which had been converted from the waulk mill in 1847, was still vulnerable. It

Table 7.2 Reported occurrence of property flooding in Morpeth 1893–1903

	11 Jun 1863	2 Nov 1863	20 Dec 1876	21 Aug 1877	22 Jan 1878	31 Dec 1878	9 Mar 1881	6 Nov 1886	7 Sep 1898	18 Oct 1898	26 Oct 1900	9 Oct 1903
High Stanners		1	2	1	1	2	1	1	2			
Olivers Mill					1		1					
Beechfield Ho.	3					1	1		1			
Low Stanners	3	1	1	1	1	1	1	1	1	1	1	1
Staithes Lane							1	1				
Bennett's Walk	3		2/1?				1	1	1	1	1	
Tenter Tce			2/1?			1						
Albert Inn	1	1	Abandoned 1868 and later demolished									
East Mill						1	1	1	1	1		1/2

1 – Flooded houses
2 – Flooded access
3 – Flooded road / gardens

now housed a menagerie and an eccentric museum displaying amongst other treasures 'portions of exhausted thunderbolts'[6]. Its ground floor was flooded. The flood of 2 November was reportedly about the same level. Albert Inn was completely surrounded: 'All houses near the river were flooded', including some at Damside affected by the Tanner's Burn. Downstream, the flood was 'a full three inches higher than that of June' at Sheepwash Mill where houses were flooded.

From 1876 to 1886 the Wansbeck suffered an extraordinary sequence of floods in every season, like many other rivers of Northumbria. The flood of December 1876 was preceded by a storm of wind and rain 'which had not been equated for about 11 years', and the river rose and subsided three times during the day. Tenants of some of the houses at the foot of the yards leading from the south side of Bridge Street had to seek shelter elsewhere and at one in the morning several residents of Low Stanners and Damside had to quit their homes. Residents at High Stanners could only reach home by circuitous routes, presumably because of flooding at the end of Oldgate Bridge (a girder bridge erected in 1872 to replace the suspension bridge).

The following summer was very wet, especially late August 1877 when rain fell almost without break for three days. Homes were flooded in High and Low Stanners where occupants had to wade more than knee-deep from their houses and, at Bennett's Walk and Tenter Terrace, residents had to requisition an omnibus to carry them home. A story is told of an unfortunate cow carried downstream four miles: 'In going over the dam head at East Mills for a short space of time she appeared drowned, only her feet visible on the surface. She was got out at Bothal Haughs quite exhausted and brought round by the aid of some whiskey'.

The January flood of 1878 was one of the largest on record and resulted from prolonged rainfall. The river level since then has only twice been exceeded. At the High Stanners it flooded, amongst others, the home of George Jeffrey, clerk to the local Board of Health, but he had sufficient warning to remove carpets and lighter furniture. Downstream, Oliver's bakehouse, Wear's mill and adjacent houses extending from the foot of Turk's Head Yard down the north side of the river were flooded: 'The inhabitants had to betake themselves and their feathered fowls to the rooms above'. One person lost four pigs. At the Low Stanners houses were flooded to three feet eight inches.

One old man Anty Cocklin lay still in the greatest composure till he found the mattress heaving beneath him. He then got up and with difficulty waded his way to the higher ground leading to Mill Square.

Water backed up the Cotting burn, flooding Mill Square and the east side of Damside. Wright's timber yard was under two feet of water. Nearby, the quay wall at Beechfield and the Willows was overtopped, covering gardens and floors of the Vineries and filling cellars. Further downstream, East Mill was flooded to a depth of three feet and the bridge at Quarry Drift colliery was twisted out of position.

Snowmelt floods followed in December 1878 and March 1881 and, although the latter was not as severe on the Wansbeck as on the Tyne and Tees, High and Low Stanners and Bennett's Walk were again flooded. At East Mill the water stood two feet deep on the floor of the mill but did not reach the house.

The frequent recurrence of flooding spurred action to help those worst affected. A riverside embankment was built at Low Stanners and residents elsewhere were provided with zinc sheets to nail over their doorways. However, these measures appear to have been ineffective as the embankment was overtopped in November 1886 and houses were flooded as before. The flood level was marginally higher than in 1881 and at East Mill the water entered the house as well as the mill where the ground floor was reported to be completely wrecked. Above the High Stanners, Sanderson's bridge which was built in 1880, the predecessor of the Skinnery bridge, had its central pier undermined and tilted, requiring major remedial works[5].

There was a gap of twelve years until September 1898 when the extraordinary thunderstorm and flash flood, described in Chapter 9, struck the catchment. However, the main effect of this storm on Morpeth was the saturation of soils so that, when prolonged heavy rain occurred the following month, much of it flowed directly into the river, causing Morpeth flooding to a level only known to have been exceeded in 1963. Three days of rain culminated in a thunderstorm on the evening of 17 October and the river reached its peak in Morpeth the following morning. Sanderson's bridge was nearly broken in two. Oliver's flour mill suffered considerable damage and in houses in Low Stanners and Staithes Lane the flood was five or six feet deep. At the East Mill house the water reached the seventh step of the stairs leading to the bedrooms. The level is engraved nearby on the doorway of an outbuilding.

A little further downstream an unexpected disaster struck T. Proudlock, a tripe preparer at Job's Well Close. His works adjoined a disused coal shaft and the weight of water broke through the shaft covering and, swirling down the opening, carried away cart, trap, watchdog, ten pigs and part of his buildings. At Sheepwash a temporary bridge damaged in September was completely destroyed.

COTTING BURN – STRIKE 1

Flooding from the Cotting (Tanner's) burn has already been noted in January 1878, mainly as the result of backing up from the Wansbeck, but on the night of Friday 26 October 1900 the burn itself caused flooding at least as severe as any the Wansbeck had so far produced.

Coastal rainfall extended from Teesside to North Northumberland. At Morpeth, sleet and snow commenced about 6 p.m. on the 26th, changed to rain about 10 p.m. and continued until next morning. The rainfall station at Cockle Park recorded 79 millimetres in sixteen hours.

Shortly after 1 a.m. on Saturday 27 the burn began to surcharge the culverts through the town, back up and overflow. It rose so suddenly that there was little time to save possessions. Water poured through the Masonic Hall and the caretaker's house from which residents escaped through a window. St James's National School was flooded as was the nave of St James's church. Sunday services were cancelled. Homes of working-class families in Copper Chare, Hiver, Flint's Yard, Stanley Cottages, Staithes Lane, Mill Square and Low Stanners (again) were flooded[7]. Seven families were sent to the Isolation Hospital on Morpeth Common and given beds and provisions. Others moved upstairs or to neighbour's homes. Garden walls were knocked down from Beggar Lane to Dark Lane.

Industries, too, suffered. Swinney's Wansbeck iron works was covered to a depth of five feet. Haswell joiners and Hallowell coachwrights were inundated as were buildings at the Pulp Mill. The *Morpeth Herald* expressed its astonishment:

No such devastation from a flood has ever been heard tell of at Morpeth and the marvel to all is that it should have been caused by the Tanner's Burn.

THE RECORD OF FLOOD STONES

The one gauging station on the Wansbeck at Mitford, just downstream from the confluence with the Font, was established in 1968. However, flood stones at Bothal Mill and East Mill provide a basis for comparing the severe Wansbeck floods of the late nineteenth century with more recent extremes. The record at Bothal Mill is the most comprehensive and, although the wall on which the levels were inscribed was demolished in the early 1980s, fortunately the levels had been surveyed previously by River Authority engineers. They are as follows:

7 Mar	1963	10.88m above Ordnance Datum
	1898	10.78m
	1878	10.37m
	1886	10.30m
17 Oct	1967	9.81m
1 Jun	1924	9.78m
	1948	9.48m

There are only two engraved stones at East Mill, for 1963 and 1898, and these confirm the supremacy of the 1963 flood, which in this case was about 0.18 metres higher than in 1898.

A QUIESCENT RIVER

The above record suggests, and a more detailed search confirms that, in contrast to the frequent events of the previous half century, the Wansbeck during the first half of the twentieth century was remarkably quiescent. Only on 9 October 1903, 1 June 1924 and on 11 January 1948 did the level rise sufficiently to flood houses. Of these the flood of June 1924 was undoubtedly the worst and came as the result of widespread and prolonged rainfall. At Morpeth 105mm of rain fell in thirty-six hours, commencing early morning of 31 May. The flood 'spoils' were divided between the Wansbeck and the Tanner's burn.

On the Wansbeck the Oldgate bridge was impassable at the Stanners end though there is no mention of property flooding there. Nine houses were flooded at Bennett's Walk, some to a depth of three feet. At East Mill the water covered the mill basement but did not reach the house.

Culvert capacities were again exceeded on the Tanner's burn. It overflowed at Swinney's foundry and also at the top of the Phoenix Yard, flooding the mayor's stables there and cottages in Corporation Yard. The water ran down Stanley Lane to Dark Lane where it divided, one half going down Staithes Lane flooding houses there and in Mill Square, and joining the Wansbeck in inundating the Low Stanners. The other stream turned left along Dark Lane and flooded a garage and gardens. Waters and Robson's mineral water factory in Stanley Terrace was flooded to four feet. Worst-affected families, mainly from the Low Stanners, spent the night in the town hall and sixty people were supplied with blankets and three meals before returning next day to their damp homes where the emergency services had been in action pumping out their houses.

The flood of 11 January 1948 was reported as the highest for twenty-four years but only roads and a 'few' houses were flooded. An event of similar severity followed on 28 August 1956 when houses in Bennett's Walk were flooded to a few inches depth.

MORPETH'S GREAT FLOOD – 6 MARCH 1963

By mid-century residents of Morpeth might have been forgiven for believing that the Wansbeck no longer posed any threat to the town. For two generations the river had only just overtopped its banks, and the memory of previous floods had all but faded. Riverside development proceeded apace. In the early decades terraced rows grew up on the floodplain along and behind Bennett's Walk. After World War I the Garden City was built on the High Stanners to house returning soldiers and people moved from the overcrowded yards of Back Riggs. In the 1930s houses extended out along Mitford Road and the bungalows of Challenor's Gardens behind Abbey Terrace were added in the early 1950s. On the Low Stanners the original often-flooded houses were demolished but new terraces developed along Staithes Lane and Wellwood Gardens. The Terrace gardens were converted to a car park with the County Library headquarters nearby backing on to the river. No riverside protection was provided. Inadvertently the town had laid the preparations for the flood disaster and the river did the rest on 7 March 1963.

The winter of 1962/3 was the coldest over England and Wales as a whole since 1740, with snow lying over most of the country for more than two months. The precipitation during January and February of about 150mm had accumulated on the Wansbeck catchment virtually without depletion by a thaw. On clear sunny days in late February, midday temperatures crept above 0°C for a few hours only to fall back at night to −10°C. The surface snow thawed but refroze at night as the pack became more solid.

The real thaw commenced on 5 March as temperatures rose above 6°C and remained high during the night. It accelerated on the 6th and 7th as successive midday temparatures reached 7°C and 9°C. Much of the melt water was initially held in the snowpack which became more and more saturated and it was not until early on the 6th that there was much change in the solidly frozen river. The ice pack began to break up, forming temporary jams against bridges and weirs. The river rose steadily during the day until 6 p.m. After a slight overnight fall in level the river surged to its unprecedented peak at 7.30 p.m. on Thursday.

On the morning of 7 March, sandbags were laid in preparation at Bennett's Walk but the river rose over the roadway at 11.30 a.m.[8]. It was soon realised that measures were futile and the evacuation commenced. By 1.30 p.m., the Goosehill area was cut off with about three feet of water outside Castle Square school (Plate 7.1). During the afternoon the flood deepened and spread to more and more streets: Mitford Road, High Stanners, Challenor's Gardens, Pretoria Avenue, Baysland, Olivers Mill (Fig 7.2) . In the late afternoon water spilled through Chantry Place into Bridge Street as the level reached nearly to the top of the arch at Telford bridge (Plate 7.2). The Presbyterian Church was surrounded and the cellars flooded. In The Terrace car park some cars were completely submerged and in Gas House Lane a bubble car bobbed in the current before being lodged against a wall. The library was flooded and books soaked.

Eight fire engines were called in to assist the evacuation and dinghies were used by police and fire services. Two policemen were rescued from the roof of the ambulance station where they had scrambled when their boat sprang a leak and sank. One of the rescuers, a butcher, had to be rescued with a boathook

Plate 7.1 Goosehill, Morpeth outside the Castle school looking toward Bennett's Walk on 7 March 1963. *Photo. A. B. Stait.*

when he fell into water eight feet deep. They told the *Morpeth Herald* it was a frightening experience at the bottom of Staithes Lane as the current had a force which could not be appreciated from the top of the street. On the south bank all the terrace housing behind Bennett's Walk to Allery Banks was awash and old people were rescued from Middle Greens where the water was five feet deep.

At an early stage telephones were put out of action at the police station and elsewhere, making the coordination of rescue more difficult. Electricity also failed in parts of the town. The high–pressure gas main carried on Stobsford bridge was submerged but survived until Saturday 9 when the weakened bank collapsed and fractured it.

Traffic came to a standstill as Oldgate bridge was closed at 2.30 p.m., cutting off access to the High Stanners, and in Bridge Street abandoned vehicles blocked the road. On the Ashington Road a mobile shop and another vehicle were swept on their sides and a bus stranded.

A reception centre for evacuees was set up in the town hall and beds and blankets were provided with aid from St John's Ambulance, the Red Cross and the Salvation Army. However, most residents returned home the next day to face the mess. Although the water had receded, the roads were covered in mud

Plate 7.2 Telford Bridge with the water approaching the top of the arches on 7 March 1963. *Photo. J. Primrose, Morpeth.*

up to two feet deep or had been torn up by the current. There was a ten-foot crater in Bennett's Walk. Silt and debris lay thick in houses as the mopping-up began. Council workmen spent long hours in clearing up at homes of elderly and disabled residents and there was also help from the RAF and many community organisations. Electrical circuits were checked, hot-air machines were brought in to dry houses, and to provide a carpet-drying service in the town hall. The fire service hosed down roads, and neighbouring councils donated the services of gulley emptiers and street sweepers.

In all, 482 houses, twenty-one shops in Bridge Street and Chantry, and factories, garages, and builders yards were affected over an area of 31.8 hectares (78.5 acres)[9]. The relief fund set up by the mayor received 350 claims for assistance, and claims of £16,000 were met. The losses of businesses and local authorities were estimated at £50,000.

From a hydrological point of view the flood was remarkable in being caused by melting snow, virtually without associated rainfall. The total rainfall over the catchment was a mere 4 mm. However, a strong wind reaching over twenty-five knots on 7 March assisted the thaw. The event provided a spur to scientific research into potential rates of snowmelt runoff whose results have been incorporated in national procedures for the design of flood defences and flood warning schemes[10].

RELIEF WORKS AND THEIR TESTING

It was clear from the devastation that major works were required to protect all those properties which had trespassed on the floodplain, and an interim scheme was prepared in haste by the Northumberland and Tyneside River Board. The construction of new concrete riverside walls at Bennett's Walk, The Terrace car park and in the vicinity of Baysland Road and Oliver's mill started in October 1964 and was completed in 1965[9]. An earth bank was also built over Allery burn with a flap valve on the outlet to the river.

It had been appreciated that these works would not provide the ultimate solution, but their efficiency was soon tested, in October 1967. This flood showed the limitations of the defences and where further work should be concentrated.

The flood of 17 October 1967 was not nearly so severe as that of 1963. The river level was generally about three feet lower, but forty-five houses were flooded (Fig 7.2). Problems as usual were centred on Bennett's Walk and the Low Stanners area. Although the river level was two feet below the top of the new flood wall at Bennett's Walk, the Church and Postern burns were unable to discharge into the main river and spilled out behind the wall, flooding eighteen houses and the lemonade factory in Goosehill (Plate 7.3). Some protection had been given, however, and the water in the street was some three feet lower than in the adjacent river.

In the Low Stanners the new flood wall adjacent to the library failed and the water swept through the gap as well as spilling over from the Cotting burn. The new library building completed the previous year was flooded to three feet but staff managed to rescue all the books by wading through an increasing depth of water to carry them upstairs. The new ambulance station and welfare clinic were also flooded as were twenty-five houses. Three houses were flooded near Oliver's mill where there was a gap in the flood defences. Although Oldgate bridge was closed to traffic and the road flooded, houses in the High Stanners escaped.

The town came to a standstill as workers, recalling 1963, rushed home to lift furniture and possessions. One unfortunate resident had had a new carpet laid on Monday afternoon only to find it under six inches of water on the morning of Tuesday 17.

The River Authority quickly set about designing further relief works along the main river and on the tributary burns. The plan was to do the works on the main river in two further stages, Stage Two in the reach downstream from Elliot Bridge; and Stage Three upstream from Elliot Bridge[11], mainly to protect the High Stanners area. The works proposed in Stage Two had three essential objectives:

1. to improve the carrying capacity of the river and reduce the water level for a given flow in the reach downstream from Telford Bridge. To this end the channel was to be widened where possible from an average of seventy to a hundred feet. The extra width was to be gained on the north bank.

2. to ensure that walls and embankments were complete and designed to protect against a repeat of the 1963 flood flow. Works included new earth embankments

Plate 7.3 The new flood wall to protect Bennett's Walk from the Wansbeck did not protect it from flooding on 17 October 1967 when the water backed up tributary burns.
Photo. A. B. Stait.

at Low Stanners, repair to the breach in the wall at the library and a river wall downstream from Oliver's Mill. These works would ensure that existing defences would not be outflanked.

3. to ensure that the tributary burns will still discharge into the Wansbeck when flow in the Wansbeck is high, rather than overspill behind the defences. This would require the culverting of the lower reaches of the Church, Postern and Allery burns to give them sufficient pressure head. Only modest changes were proposed for the Cotting burn, with the raising of the right bank wall in the lower reaches.

The works on the main river (Items 1 and 2) were built by the River Authority in 1969 and that on the tributaries (Item 3) by Morpeth Borough Council. Costs were £67,000 and £75,300 respectively.

There was no intention to carry out Stage Three above Elliot Bridge until the new bridge at Oldgate was completed (1970). But when residents were canvassed about the scheme a large majority of occupants of High Stanners felt that it was preferable to suffer the risk of infrequent flooding than to lose the amenity of a view of the river. The works were therefore scaled down and consisted only of the building of a flood bank to protect Pretoria Avenue (1973) and the raising of the Elliot Bridge to take it clear of the 1963 flood level[12]. With the completion of this phase, 398 of the 482 houses flooded in 1963 were reckoned to have been protected. The remaining eighty-four were in the High Stanners and along the Mitford Road.

THE COTTING BURN STRIKES AGAIN

The design for Stage Two had just been finished, with the modest recommendations for the lower reaches of the Cotting burn, when in the early morning of 13 September 1968 the tributary again unleashed its fury on the town. At Cockle Park just outside the catchment, 72mm of rain were recorded in less than four hours.

The 1900 flood was only a vague recollection of an octagenarian. The pattern of flooding was remarkably similar: the culverts and channel in the upper part of the town became filled to capacity and the pent-up water escaped and cascaded through streets and houses. A lake was formed behind a wall at the former girls' grammar school in Newgate Street. The wall suddenly gave way and released a massive wave. The school caretaker watched in horror as the wave lifted a 'mobile' classroom from its footings and threw it against a wall. Water crashed through the drill hall in Copper Chare breaking doors and windows. Water and debris thundered in the tunnel below and the pressure caused the tunnel roof to collapse outside St James's church. Water spurted out and added to the surface flow, flooding St James's and the adjacent Methodist church and church hall where the water was six feet deep and covered two pianos.

Houses in Maritime Place and Howard Road were flooded. The water swept over Dacre Street and Swinney's foundry (Plate 7.4) where it picked up fifteen tons of coke and scattered it along Stanley Terrace, finally reaching the more familiar scenes of flooding in Staithes Lane and Wellwood Gardens. Fortunately, neither the Wansbeck nor the Church and Postern burns were at an exceptionally high level.

A report was prepared the following year by the River Authority[13], suggesting alternative solutions to this flood problem. One expensive possibility was the enlarging of culverts and channel for 1200 metres but the favoured solution was a diversion channel to carry the entire flow into the Wansbeck near Dogger Bank, at a point where the distance between Cotting burn and the Wansbeck is only 110 metres. This would exclude flood flows from the entire urban area. Since the work was not on a main river the responsibility lay with the borough council but, for reasons which I have been unable to determine, neither alternative was approved or carried out. Morpeth remains vulnerable to an intense storm on the headwaters of the burn.

FINAL CHECKS

There were no major floods on the Wansbeck during the 1970s. Floods in 1981, 1982 and 1992 provided the most recent tests of the defences. In the flood of 3 January 1982, 60mm of rain fell on a snow-covered catchment with the ground still frozen from the severe frosts of December 1981. It thus had a greater discharge than the floods of 2 March 1981 and 1 April 1992 although these had higher rainfall.

None of these floods had flow rates as great as the 1963 flood but all were greater than October 1967. Nevertheless, damage was much less than in 1967. Only a single house above Oldgate bridge (Dyers Cottage) was flooded in 1981,

Plate 7.4 Dacre Street, Morpeth, submerged by flooding from the Cotting burn on 13 September 1968.

four were flooded in 1992 and nine houses and the Social Club in 1982. The defences were effective at Low Stanners and Bennett's walk although there was some anxiety on 1 April 1992 when the roadway began to crumble at Bennett's Walk, owing to the water pressure in the Church burn culvert underneath. East Mill was flooded on all three occasions and Mr Yeales reported a level of twenty-seven inches in his home in 1982 compared with forty-five inches in 1963.

At the new Oldgate bridge water levels in 1982 rose alarmingly close to the top of the bridge arch (Plate 7.5). A slightly bigger flood or blockage by debris would cause the arch to fill completely and then levels upstream would rise rapidly as the water backed up.

Although such an occurrence is likely to be very infrequent (perhaps on average once in thirty years) the possibility demonstrates the continuing need for effective flood warning, a service now provided by the National Rivers Authority. Flood warning for the vulnerable areas along the Cotting burn is more difficult as the time from rainfall to runoff is very short. This is one of the few sites in Northumbria which might benefit from the development of a radar rainfall system to forecast and measure the intensity of rainfall.

Morpeth, like Darlington, is an example of a town where a period of unchecked development on the flood plain has been followed by a succession of works to protect low-lying property. Whilst such works have been effective, they have also greatly diminished the natural amenity of the riverside to the

town. One can immediately point to the contrast in the popularity on a sunny summer day between the unprotected High Stanners river bank and the inaccessible river below Bennett's Walk. Between Oldgate and Baysland, embankments have more effectively combined amenity and flood alleviation and there is still scope in the reach below Telford bridge to improve the appearance and give access to the water's edge within the banks without jeopardising the flood defence.

THE BLYTH – A SUMMARY

In the catchment of the river Blyth the main flooding has occurred along its principal tributary, the river Pont. In the past, agricultural land was regularly inundated near Stamfordham and on the flat fens of Prestwick Carrs, east of Ponteland. Two changes have reduced the frequency of, but by no means eliminated, such flooding. Firstly the stream has been effectively beheaded by the diversion of the headwaters (twenty-three square kilometres of the catchment) towards the Whittle Dene reservoirs to augment resources for water supply to Newcastle. Below the diversion point, east of Matfen, there is no flow in the Pont channel down to the next tributary junction, and flood flows are greatly reduced. The second change has been to the river channel which was extensively deepened and widened during the immediate post-war period by the Northumberland Rivers Catchment Board.

In 1925 modifications were made to the bridge in Ponteland to increase its flood capacity. River engineers believed that this work had virtually eliminated the risk of flooding at The Diamond road junction, where there had previously been frequent flooding (eg 1900, 1903)[14]. However, the storm of 1 April 1992 demonstrated the continuing vulnerability of houses in the vicinity when the waters again spread out across the road and into the sheltered homes of Athol House, where 17 properties were flooded. On the same occasion three houses at Riverside on the Darras Hall estate were flooded up to a depth of 0.3m. The same houses had received early warning of their vulnerability when the site was flooded before construction was complete on 29 March 1979, and flooding was repeated to the same level following the thaw on 3 January 1982.

Along the main river Blyth from its source at Kirkheaton to the estuary there is no record of any flooding of property although riverside meadows are frequently covered and the road adjacent to Bellasis bridge may become impassable.

REFERENCES
 1. Hodgson J. *History of Morpeth*, (Newcastle upon Tyne, 1832, reprinted 1973)
 2. Fergusson, J. *Morpeth from the accession to the Jubilee of Queen Victoria*, (Morpeth 1887, reprinted 1985)
 3. Northumberland County, Quarter Sessions Order Books, Mss, Northumberland County Record Office
 4. Tweddle, A. H. Town *Trails for Morpethians* no 1.
 5. Ibid., no 3
 6. Ibid., no 7
 7. Anon. 'Heavy rainfall in Durham and Northumberland on October 26th 1900', *Symons Monthly Meteorological Magazine*, (1900)
 8. Borough of Morpeth. Borough Surveyor's Report of the 1963 Flood, Borough Engineer, (1963)
 9. Northumbrian River Authority, Morpeth Flood Protection Scheme, Stage 2, Engineers Report, (1968)
10. Natural Environment Research Council *Flood Studies Report*, vol. 2, ch. 7, 'Snowmelt' (5 vols, London, 1975)
11. Northumbrian River Authority, Morpeth Flood Protection Scheme, Stage 3, Engineers Report, (1969)
12. Ibid., Morpeth Flood Protection Scheme, Stage 2 (Extension), Engineers Report, (1972)
13. Ibid., Cotting Burn Flood By-pass, Morpeth, Engineers Report, (1969)
14. Almond, L., Stobbs, R. and Ponteland Local History Society (Me and Him with help from Them), *Ponteland, One Thousand Years of History*.

Fig 8.1 The Till and neighbouring rivers of north Northumberland.

8. CHEVIOT STREAMS
– TILL, COQUET AND ALN

Land of singing waters
And winds from off the sea
God bring me to Northumberland
The land where I would be
Wilfred Wilson Gibson Northumberland

The streams of the Border country radiate like the spokes of a giant wheel from The Cheviot, the highest point, at over eight hundred metres of the Cheviot range (Fig 8.1). To the north the Bowmont Water and College burn join as the river Glen. To the north-east, the Harthope and Carey burns merge to become the Wooler water and, in the east, the Breamish rises above Bleakhope and descends eastward through the Ingram valley before turning north to be renamed the river Till at Bewick mill. As the old saying goes:

Foot of Breamish and head of Till
Meet together at Bewick mill.

In their middle courses, these rivers skirt the Cheviot massif before converging in the great flat tract of land north of Wooler, from which the Till continues its meandering course to the Tweed between Coldstream and Norham.

Southward from The Cheviot (Fig 8.2) flow the Alwin and Usway burns (pronounced Oosey), tributaries of the Coquet which itself rises further west on Brownshart Law and traces an eastward course past Alwinton, Holystone and Rothbury, through Felton and Warkworth, to the sea at Amble.

The river Aln rises between the Coquet and Breamish on the margin of the Cheviots and threads its gentle course eastwards. It falls only one hundred and fifty metres on its journey from its source above Alnham to Alnmouth. It is a mere 'baby on a rushy bed'.

Cheviot rivers do not have the same record of inundation of property as those from the Pennine uplands. Their vigour and destructiveness are displayed in a quite different way, in the movement of sediment and erosion of banks and river bed on a scale possibly not equalled anywhere else in England and Wales. This reputation for erosion and regular flooding of extensive areas of agricultural land has fortunately discouraged development on the floodplain.

Cheviot streams owe their courses, their very characteristic valleys and their flood response, to events of great antiquity, for they show the controlling hand of geology more distinctly than most Northumbrian rivers. The rocks of the Cheviots were formed in two main episodes of igneous activity[1,2]. The first

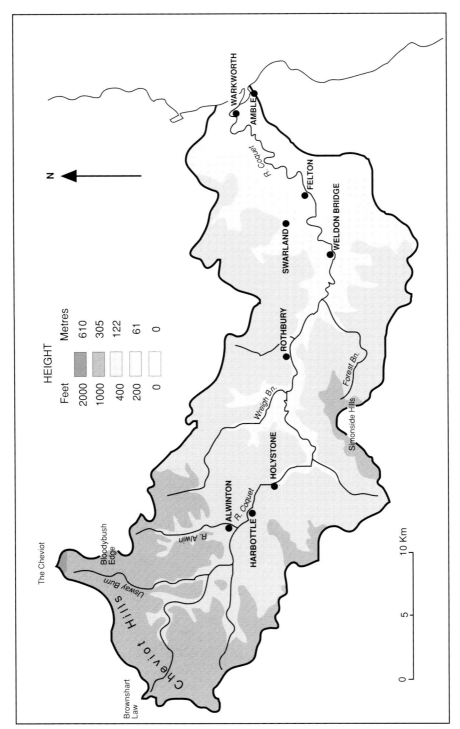

HEIGHT

Feet	Metres
2000	610
1000	305
400	122
200	61
0	0

N

The Cheviot

Brownshart Law

Cheviot Hills

Bloodybush Edge

Uswhay Burn

R. Alwin

ALWINTON

R. Coquet

HARBOTTLE

HOLYSTONE

Wreigh Bn.

ROTHBURY

Forest Bn.

Simonside Hills

SWARLAND

WELDON BRIDGE

FELTON

R. Coquet

AMBLE

WARKWORTH

0   5   10 Km

Fig 8.2 The river Coquet and its catchment.

occurred around four hundred million years ago in the geological period known as the Devonian when Cheviot volcanoes poured out ash and rock fragments (pyroclasts) and then andesitic lavas. These andesites are now the most widespread Cheviot rocks. The second episode, some millions of years later but still within the Devonian period, was the intrusion of a granite stock into the lavas. Through long-continued weathering and erosion, the granite has been exposed on the surface and now forms the bedrock over a near-circular area of about seventy square kilometres centred on Hedgehope Hill.

These two main rock types have quite different topography and vegetation. The more resistant granite forms the high inner plateau, including The Cheviot itself. Here the headwater valleys, like the Common burn and the Breamish above Linhope, are broad and shallow, and the acidic rock and associated soils support peat and heather moorland. The flat top of the Cheviot is a desolate boggy place and the summit cairn is approached at the expense of waterlogged boots and weary legs. There is little infiltration of rainfall here and runoff to streams is rapid, as in the Pennines.

In contrast, the more typical Cheviot landscape on andesitic lavas has deep and steep-sided valleys with occasional rock outcrops and trains of pink screes descending to the valley floor (Plate 8.1). Hill tops and valley sides are usually grass- and bracken-covered and the less acid parent rock allows better drained soils to develop. Therefore, in spite of the steep slopes, there are longer delays from rainfall to river flow than on the granite rock or the Pennine headwaters of Tyne and Tees, and a smaller proportion of the rainfall is released immediately to the river in flood flows.

Glaciation, too, has had a strong impact on the Cheviot valleys, deepening the main channels in the uplands, diverting them by blocking their pre-glacial channels in the lowlands, and creating new channels as the ice melted and released vast quantities of water under and away from the ice sheets. Some of the most distinct landforms were created in the last stages of the Ice Age when local valley glaciers moved out from the hills, and the resulting steep-sided headwater basins of Henhole and the Bizzle west of the Cheviot resemble the ice-carved corries of the Lake District. A clear example of glacial diversion is the Bowmont water: that stream follows the Yetholm fault northwards to within five kilometres of the river Tweed but near Mindrum it was diverted east by blocking glacial deposits and now takes a more incised route between Housedon and Kilham hills and eventually reaches the Tweed by the rivers Glen and Till, after a journey of thirty-six kilometres from Mindrum.

The channels produced by glacial meltwater are curious but common features of the Cheviot landscape especially on the north-east and south-east margins. The channels converge towards the middle Breamish around Ilderton where vast irregular deposits of sand and gravel have been distributed. The channels are often now abandoned but show a deeply V-cut profile and unlike normal rivers may rise and fall along the channel and may branch and rejoin – a strong indication of an enclosed formation beneath the ice sheet.

An inheritance of the Ice Age which continues to affect the character of Cheviot rivers today is the vast quantity of sediment dumped on hillsides and

Plate 8.1 The steep-sided valley of the upper Coquet near Bygate in late winter. *Photo D. Archer.*

Plate 8.2 Reflections on the lower Till near Heaton mill. *Photo D. Archer.*

valley floors, a constant supply of material to be reworked by modern streams in flood. Thus Cheviot streams are mainly gravel-bed rivers with banks that can move laterally through erosion. Migration of gravel and boulder beds downstream may choke the channel and force flood water over the banks. The maintenance of channels in North Northumberland by clearing and sometimes dredging has thus been a priority of the National Rivers Authority, and its predecessor organisations from the days of the catchment boards in the 1940s, in order to alleviate flooding and discourage erosion.

Nevertheless, overbank flooding is a natural feature of these rivers and, even in the headwater streams with steep valley sides, there is a characteristic ribbon of flat active floodplain across which the flood spreads on average every two or three years. In this respect, tributary valleys north and south are similar. Further downstream, in the middle reaches of the Till and Coquet, floodplains widen considerably. The river Coquet leaves the Cheviot igneous rocks near Alwinton and, in places between Holystone and Rothbury, it has created a broad alluvial valley over five hundred metres in width. The old racecourse, now the golf course, overlooked from the south by the Fell Sandstone ridge of the Simonside Hills, is regularly inundated.

Just below Rothbury the Coquet is confined in a rocky channel and roars over the rapids at the Thrum. From that point the valley floor is nowhere as wide as it is upstream nor is flooding as extensive, though it does at times break out onto the road at Pauperhaugh on the way to Weldon Bridge. From Rothbury to Warkworth near the mouth of the river, a distance of thirty-three kilometres, only a few buildings are vulnerable in extreme conditions.

In their middle courses, the river Breamish below Ingram and Bowmont Water below Yetholm have similar meandering channels in a broad plain. The floodplain on the Breamish is broken only in short reaches below Powburn and near West Horton where the river cuts through a ridge of Fell Sandstone. Tributary burns in this reach also have a history of overspilling their banks at Powburn and Lilburn. Minor roads and bridges at Brandon, Powburn, Bewick and Chatton have been affected.

The rivers Till, Glen and Wooler Water join on the wide, flat Milfield plain, said to have been a lake basin at the end of the glacial period (though the geological evidence for this is limited). During major floods, this area has become a lake again with flood water stretching from Wooler to Doddington and from Kirknewton to Weetwood.

Like the Coquet, the valley of the Till narrows in its lower reaches and, downstream from Etal, meanders similar to those at Durham are incised into the bedrock. The still-incised valley joins the river Tweed just below the splendid span of the medieval Twizel bridge.

LEGAL INTERLUDE

For centuries, the tide of war and feud swept across North Northumberland as Scots and English in turn gained the ascendancy. The long story of 'blood and fire, violence, lawlessness and suffering' finally flickered out in the Jacobite risings of the eighteenth century. Although the border was eventually fixed in the present form between two reconciled neighbours, Scottish law, which differs in many respects from English, has occasionally strayed south of the border, with implications for river management.

If you look again at a map of the Borders (Fig 8.1) you will note that the national boundary nearly coincides with the watershed between the Tweed on the one side and the North Tyne and Coquet on the other. However, on approaching the Cheviot, the boundary strikes out northward along a minor divide towards the Tweed, leaving the greater part of the Till, with the exception of its tributary, the upper Bowmont Water, in England. From Carham to Paxton, a distance of twenty-eight kilometres, the boundary follows the centre line of the Tweed before cutting north-east leaving Berwick and most of the tidal reach of the Tweed in England.

The disparity between catchment and administrative boundaries creates problems for river management with the possibility of different rules being applied on different tributaries of the same river. However, the division between English and Scottish jurisdiction is not uniformly applied across different river functions. Thus Scottish law applies with respect to water resources for the whole of the Tweed catchment, including the Till and other minor English tributaries. The National Rivers Authority has no statutory control over the amount of water which can be taken from the river Till, unlike other English rivers where the control of abstractions is exercised through licensing. Similarly, the Tweed Commissioners, a statutory body established under Acts of Parliament of 1857, 1859 and 1969 has responsibility for fisheries within the entire Tweed catchment.

In contrast, for flood defence and pollution prevention, English law, applied through the National Rivers Authority, extends to the national boundary. Thus, for example, the National Rivers Authority has responsibility for promoting schemes to alleviate flooding of land and property and for the construction and maintenance of flood alleviation structures on the Till (excepting part of the Bowmont), whilst it is the Scottish regional Councils who hold similar but somewhat reduced responsibilities on the Scottish tributaries. For pollution prevention and river water quality, the Scottish counterpart of the NRA is the Tweed River Purification Board. This rather confusing division of jurisdiction and responsibilities was confirmed in the Water Acts 1989 and 1991.

DESTRUCTION OF MILLS AND BRIDGES
Owing to the limited risk to houses, early information on flooding in the northern rivers of Northumberland most often related to damage to, or loss of, mills and bridges. Although strictly outside our area of study there are very ancient records of flooding on the river Tweed. According to Hoveden[3], Berwick bridge was destroyed in 1199 and a later bridge was washed away in 1294[4].

The earliest reports of flooding on the Coquet and Aln were nearly five hundred years later. A new bridge was constructed at Weldon mill during the summer months of 1744 following an order of the Northumberland quarter sessions. Advertisement of the proposals appeared in the *Newcastle Journal* of 7

January 1744. The bridge had a brief span for it was carried away on 4 October of the same year after 'excessive rains'. That flood had been preceded by another only two weeks earlier when the *Journal* reported 'three or four persons drowned in the Cocket river' and a lad of eighteen drowned in a tributary of the river Aln in attempting to ford a swollen burn. The same floods caused havoc at the mills of Alnwick. Tate[5] reports the rebuilding of mills in 1744-6 and the repair of breaches in the mill dam and its later reconstruction in 1746-9. The loss of the mills was especially inconvenient at a time when increased output was demanded from Alnwick to supply the army in Scotland suppressing the Jacobite '45 rebellion.

On the river Coquet the replacement bridge at Weldon Bridge had limited success lasting only until 24 August 1752 when it was reported washed out. At the same time the Coquet 'swept down several hundred fothers of corn'. In spite of Dixon's claim that the only bridges on the Coquet in 1810 were those at Warkworth, Felton and Rothbury[6]. it is likely that Weldon bridge was again replaced well before that date. The present structure bears the same architectural features (projecting keystones and pierced spandrels) as Coldstream bridge on the river Tweed, built in 1763, and probably dates from about that time.

The earliest flood records on the Till are provided by the Delaval papers of the Ford Estate[7] The estates at Ford and Etal lie along the river Till as it leaves the flat land of the Milfield plain and enters the Till gorge. The steepening channel provided the necessary head to power a series of mills. Of these, only the corn mill at Heatherslaw now remains as a visitor centre. The Delaval papers record the demise of several mills and bridges. In the earliest account John Oxley the estate manager writes to Sir John Delaval, his absent squire, in London about two floods in quick succession in 1763:

24 September 1763

There was a high flood in the river last Thursday which swept away a great deal of corn from Ewart and from farmers up the water. There was about sixty draughts employed last Wednesday afternoon dragging out the corn and hay at Ewart, Fenton etc but the water rose so quickly they could only get half of it out.

6 October 1763

Last Monday there was the greatest flood . . . that has been for a century past and have done more damage by carrying off sheep and corn than will be known for some time. . . . There is not one bit of her (the Fulling mill) left – Mr Carrs Corn mill at Eatel is entirely gone, but your Honours Corn mill at Ford have not received the least hurt altho the water was two feet deep within one of the mill houses. . . . Mr Carr's footbridge also gone which stood at the bottom of Mr Thom's haugh.

The floods of 8 November 1770 caused extensive damage on the rivers Till and Aln, but there are no records of flooding on the Coquet. Joseph Oxley at Ford Castle writes:

Much Honoured Sir, we have had an extraordinary high flood which has done considerable damage in this Neighbourhood; four mills at Alnwick belong to his Grace, and two more near this place are all swept away – Nothing much happened to your

Mills and Forge altho the water rose to the second Eve slate in the forge. The Great Boat was carried from Heaton to Spittal which with great Dificqualty we got home to the Forge this week and the 4 large logs which was at Berwick, bought for the Bridge was after some trouble saved from the Wreak and is now upon an eminence safe.

Tate details the position at Alnwick:

The fulling mill and the bleach fields are gone. The Town, the Holme Abbey and the Wythorpe mills have been swept away and there remains on the river only the Abbey and the Denwick mill.

The High or Wheat mill was also lost in spite of the recent rebuilding after a lower flood in 1767. Homes were also inundated, for Tate records that after this flood, mills and cottages by the water were taken down.

The dam above Alnwick's medieval bridge gave way and the river eroded the bridge footings on the south bank so that the bridge was described as 'considerably shrunk'. Its condition gradually became worse and on 10 December the Corporation engaged John Shepard and paid him three shillings to watch the bridge and to give travellers notice of the danger[8]. The Corporation were justified in their misgivings for on 15 December the southern arch fell into the river leaving the others in a tottering condition. Repairs were carried out but the whole structure had become unsound, and the chamberlain and council, in appealing for a replacement the following year, informed the justice of the peace that 'the county bridge at Alnwick is in a ruinous condition and from the late breaches, the passage over it is hazardous, especially for carriages'.

The bridge suffered one last attack by the river on 24 September 1772 before being abandoned. The foundation stone of the new bridge, the Lion bridge, was laid the following year in August. The chosen site was one hundred feet upstream from the medieval bridge. It was still under construction the following winter when floodwaters overtopped the bridge piers on 20 December and caused serious damage. Further north at Belford a bridge was swept away.

The Border rivers escaped serious loss in the floods of November 1771 which had been so serious on the Tyne, Wear and Tees. The Delaval papers record 'very high flood but the Boats, Mills and Forge are all safe'. However, in the flood of September 1772, the *Newcastle Journal* provides the earliest report of bridge failure in the Till catchment. The Breamish washed away the middle arch of the new bridge on the turnpike road to Wooler, presumably at Powburn. In the same flood, the centre arch of a bridge being built over the Bowmont at Mindrum mill was destroyed. The ford nearby continued in use and, just before the end of October that year, coach travellers from Kelso to Newcastle had a narrow escape when a horse drowned and they were trapped in mid-stream. They were taken out of the coach windows on ropes. In the 1790s the main road bridge at Wooler was twice carried away, first on 22 October 1791 and again on 21 September 1796. The next reference is in 1807 from the Delaval papers:

6 September 1807

. . . the wood bridge at Ford was this day entirely swept away, it being a very great flood, luckily no-one was hurt. The water is higher than ever I (Thomas Fitzwalter) saw it since I have been at Ford . . . it is very much doubted whether the Stone Bridge will stand or not as it has shrunk in several places and several parts has been taken down and put up again, but it is feared the foundation has given way but the water is not low enough to examine it thoroughly.

It is evident that the stone bridge damaged in 1807 did not survive intact. The present bridge probably rebuilt at that time contains the remnants of its predecessor only in the ribbed vaulting in the land arch on the west side.

THE RECORD OF THE NINETEENTH CENTURY

During the early nineteenth centry, the Border rivers were too far away from the regional newspapers in Newcastle to attract much notice. Even when the *Berwick Advertiser* commenced publication in 1808 it was naturally enough most concerned about the Tweed. The most serious events on the Till and Coquet merited only passing notice and it is difficult to establish comparative magnitudes. The following summary shows the continued vulnerability of agricultural land.

DATE	RIVER TILL	RIVERS COQUET AND ALN
16 Aug. 1827	Till 'never so high in living memory', at one time 14ft above normal. A new stone bridge on the College near Kirknewton washed away. Ford bridge covered for 24 hrs and battlements washed away. Flood swept away many acres of land.	No information
13 June 1828	Damage reported at Chatton and Doddington with loss of hay and corn.	Coquet overflowed banks and caused agricultural losses.
2 Dec. 1828	Following heavy rainfall there was the the greatest flood on the Tweed for upwards of 20, some say 40, years. [cf. 1782]. *Berwick Advertiser* reports Jed, Oxnam Water and Kale overflowed bank but no record for Till.	Coquet 'higher than ever remembered'. Many houses in Rothbury flooded, some up to chamber windows. Occupants rescued with difficulty. When flood subsided salmon found stranded in gardens. Poacher drowned in upper Coquet.

DATE			RIVER TILL	RIVERS COQUET AND ALN
12	Feb.	1831	Tweed and all tributaries in exceptional flood following snowstorm and thaw. Norham flooded – an occurrence only once equalled since[9]. No specific information on Till.	No written information but engraved flood mark on the Coquet at the Hermitage, Warkworth, suggests the flood was the highest in the last 200 yrs.
25	Aug.	1834	Breamish flooded at Branton. Two fishermen drowned.	No information.
15	Sep.	1839	Many hundreds of acres flooded north of Wooler. Embankments swept away. Immense damage by Glen between Newton and Till confluence to dykes, bridges and corn in stock. On Bowmont Water, bridge between two Yetholms saved by 'masses of stone thrown in where the danger lay'. However, Tweed at Coldstream 6 feet 10 inches lower than in 1831.	Heavy rain with easterly gales. Haughs covered. 50 sheep lost near Rothbury. Coquet at Felton covered with sheaves for more than 2 hours.
7	Oct.	1841	'Wooler Water was very large'.	No information
20	Aug.	1845	Till much swollen. Road from Wooler to Doddington impassable.	Coquet: No information. Aln: Two farm workers drowned at West Bolton. Much loss of crops and livestock.
28	Sep.	1856	Vale of Till completely inundated. Dykes at Ewart, Doddington and the Fentons broken in several places and crops covered. Water one foot deep in a house in Fenton.	Coquet and Aln overflowed their banks.

DATE	RIVER TILL	RIVERS COQUET AND ALN
Nov. 1863	Tollbridge at Coldgate mill swept away.	Referred to in flood of 1839.
3 Oct. 1872	No information.	Rainfall observer at Brinkburn notes that Coquet was at its highest since 1839.
28 Apr. 1876	Till overflowed. Road from Chatton to Chillingham impassable.	Coquet: rose with alarming rapidity and all low-lying land drowned. A bridge being erected one mile west of Rothbury was washed away. Aln: Flint mill near Bilton surrounded.
20 Dec. 1876	No information.	Some considerable time since Rothbury so flooded. Rothbury race course quite covered. Coquet running with a very strong current from bank to brae. Aln flooded farm land and road.
20 Aug. 1877	Till overflowed its banks. (Many houses flooded in Belford from Belford Burn.)	Coquet and tributaries much with agricultural losses.
31 Dec. 1878	Rain and thaw with westerly gales following a snow storm. Extensive flooding of land and roads including Till bridge at Doddington, Weetwood and Ewart bridge.	Coquet six inches higher than in great flood of Nov. 1863. Haughs above Rothbury a complete sheet of water. More than half Donkin's auction yard submerged. Houses flooded. The suspension bridge recently erected at Thrum mill carried away.

DATE	RIVER TILL	RIVERS COQUET AND ALN
22 July 1879	Breamish overflowed banks near Harehope and many 100 acres of corn and turnips under water. Till impassable at Chillingham bridge. (Belford again flooded.)	No information.
15 Sep. 1880	Wooler Water destroyed footbridges at Coldgate and Earle mill. Till flooded road at Doddington bridge.	Coquet highest since 1878. Donkin's auction yard, Rothbury, three-quarters submerged. Great loss of hay and corn.
9 Mar. 1881	No information.	Coquet extensively over-flowed after a thaw. However, damage limited to a few gardens only.
6 Nov. 1886	Till overflowed from Weetwood bridge to Ewart. Bridges impassable.	Rain with north-east gale. Haughs above Rothbury covered and houses in malt-ing yard flooded to 2 feet depth. At the Fenwick's house at Brinkburn Priory, water entered through lower windows. At Felton 'reached greater height than these last 9 years'. Houses flooded to 3 feet at The Stanners, Wark-worth. Houses flooded in Alnwick
22 Nov. 1890	Young woman (Peggy Bell) drowned in upper Breamish as footbridge failed near Brandon and river course altered.	No information.

DATE	RIVER TILL	RIVERS COQUET AND ALN
21 Sep. 1891	Upper Breamish again in flood. Damaged county bridge at Powburn. (Replacement single span girder bridge completed in 1892 at a cost of 2,000.) Footbridge at Brandon again failed. Bowmont Water said to be a highest for at least 19 years.	No information.
2 July 1893	Thunderstorms over Cheviots affecting upper Breamish. (see Chapter 9).	Thunderstorms over Cheviots affecting Usway and Alwin. (see Chapter 9).
18 Oct. 1898	Glen and Breamish in high flood. Peggy Bell's bridge washed away. Foundations of new iron bridge at Ingram threatened. Powburn bridge jeopardised by destruction of a weir downstream.	Thropton bridge on Wreigh burn damaged and impassable. Two footbridges between Tosson and Rothbury swept away. Several houses flooded at Rothbury malting yard. A man employed as river-watcher fell through damaged wire bridge at Fishlocks and drowned.

THE ALN IN SPATE

On 26 October 1900 a storm of driving snow and rain brought the worst flooding on the river Aln for over a century and conditions were also severe on the Coquet and Till as they were on coastal streams further south (Chapters 6 and 7). The storm was predominantly coastal and rainfall in excess of sixty millimetres was recorded from North Yorkshire to near the Scottish border (Fig 8.3). At Alnwick Castle, 93.2mm – more than a tenth of the annual total – fell in a single day. The resulting floods were made worse by the simultaneous release of rainwater and melting snow into the river channel.

As in earlier floods in the Aln, low-lying farm land was submerged, but this time much more extensively and all the tributaries were full. At Broomhouse farm on the Eglingham burn, forty sheep were drowned. As the swollen river rushed through the Duke of Northumberland's estate in Hulne Park, it swept away three bridges, the Swing bridge, the Monk's bridge and the Duchess's bridge[10]. The Abbey, Abbey mills and the Abbey Lodge grounds were

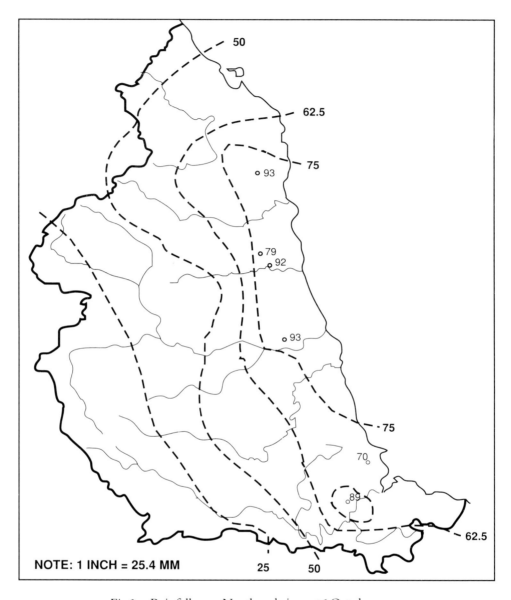

NOTE: 1 INCH = 25.4 MM

Fig 8.3 Rainfall over Northumbria on 26 October 1900.

inundated and there was damage to the horseshoe waterfall. The normal trickle in the Watch burn became a torrent and, aided by the Aln, flooded the Duke's dairy. Several pigs were drowned in adjacent buildings. The burn then swept behind the cottages in Canongate. The dynamo buildings supplying electricity for lighting at Alnwick Castle were flooded and machinery damaged.

Two miles downstream Peter's bridge at Denwick mill was carried away and the water was six inches deep in the basement of the mill house. The Alndyke and Hawkhill haughs were covered and water reached within one foot of the soffit of Hawkhill bridge. At Flint mill across the river from Hawkhill, the farmer lost four cattle and the basement of his house was flooded knee-deep. At Lesbury the water overtopped the road bridge, the road was flooded to a depth of three feet, and all traffic to Alnwick came to a halt. A nearby footbridge was washed away. The effects were severe right down to the estuary and there was damage at Waterside House.

It is likely that the 1900 flood on the Aln was the worst since the 1770s and only the flood of 1 April 1992 has approached it in height. On the Coquet and Till the severity was reduced by the comparatively small contribution from the uplands. No flooding was reported at Rothbury but conditions became progressively worse downstream. The gas house at Felton and Morwick mill were flooded and, at the Hermitage, Warkworth, the peak level is recorded by two engraved marks. On the Till the only serious damage was at Ilderton where a bridge spanning the Lil burn became unsafe through the washing-away of the supporting embankment.

THE GREAT BORDER FLOODS

Like many other Northumbrian rivers in the early part of the twentieth century the Border rivers had little spectacular flooding. Even the autumn floods of 1903, serious further south, were less severe than those in 1898 and 1900. Thunderstorms brought localised flooding on the upper Coquet on 9 June 1907 when six houses were flooded in the malting yard at Rothbury and fifty sheep, caught unawares on the Rothbury racecourse, were found dead at Lady's bridge. There were further reports of flooding on the Till in September 1926 and twice in the spring of 1934, and on the Coquet the flood of 12 March 1934 was said to have flooded 'thousands of acres of land' at the end of an exceptional drought. The Coquet Fishery Board reported exceptional flood conditions in February 1941 from melting snow, but the event went unrecorded elsewhere because of the war.

In the late 1940s, however, there were serious floods every year from 1946 to 1949 and that of 13 August 1948 was on a scale not previously witnessed. With the passage of time, the events have merged in the minds of residents and are now simply referred to as the Border Floods[11,12].

The first of these floods occurred following torrential rain on the night of 12 to 13 August 1946, with daily totals of 75mm being recorded at several places on Breamish, Wooler and Coquet catchments.

Worst hit was Rothbury where tributary streams on the north side of the valley became roaring torrents. Residents were roused from sleep by the sound of boulders carried down the Coplish burn. Tumbleton dam at Cragside was overtopped and nearly washed away (see Chapter 10). In the main street, water was four feet deep, flooding Martin's Bank, the Queen's Head hotel and many houses. In the morning, sediment lay three feet deep against doorways and German prisoners were brought in to shovel it away.

On the Breamish, eleven houses were flooded in Powburn and South

Hedgeley and one family had to retreat upstairs when the water reached the level of the table top. At Skirl Naked on the Harthope burn, fifty campers had an unpleasant surprise when a sudden surge in the level swept their belongings into the swollen river.

The following year a thaw brought flooding after the protracted winter of 1947. The effects were more widespread but not as acute as the previous year. Much agricultural land was affected as flood banks on the Glen and Till were breached but the flooding was checked by night frosts and snow remained widespread on high ground until late in April.

There were two floods in 1948. The first on 11 January, also resulting from melting snow accompanied by rain, was more severe on the Coquet where there was widespread inundation of the floodplain from Holystone to Rothbury including the racecourse. Further downstream on the road to Weldon Bridge, the water was three feet deep on the road below Thrum mill and also blocked traffic at Pauperhaugh. On the Till the road from Wooler to Doddington was under water for 250 yards.

But it was the floods of 12 August 1948 that are most frequently remembered for their destructive power. The weather of early August 1948 was wetter than usual. Rainfall totals of more than 30 mm over most of the Borders on 7 August left the soils well primed for runoff when the big rains came. On 11 August a shallow depression moved slowly east across the Midlands, reaching the southern North Sea early on the 12th. The easterly airstream and associated, nearly stationary, warm front to the north of this system brought heavy rains first to Yorkshire and Durham and then unprecedented totals in the Border region.

The rainfall commenced at 10 p.m. on the 11th at Howick Hall near Alnwick and over the next twenty-four hours a total of 110 mm fell, with the most intense rain between 9 a.m. and 2 p.m. on the 12th. Further north along the Tweed, the heaviest rain fell some hours later. The highest recorded daily total was at Carham Hall near Cornhill with 158.8 mm on the 12th. An area of over two thousand square kilometres had a daily rainfall of over 100mm (Fig 8.4). Only two previous storms in England and Wales had greater areas at the intensity (Bruton in Somerset on 28 June 1917 and East Anglia on 26 August 1912). Some parts of the Tweed valley received a third of their annual rainfall in six days.

The Tweed itself was at its highest ever level, exceeding the great flood of 1831 by six inches at Floors castle, Kelso, and by four inches at Coldstream, but devastation was reported on both sides of the border with floods in the Till and its tributaries and in all the small coastal streams of north Northumberland.

The most impressive flooding on the Till was at the confluence of the Glen where six thousand acres were under water to a depth of several feet, with only the thin curved line of the flood embankment top, breached in many places, breaking the surface. (The embankments had been first built by the Culley family at Akeld in the early nineteenth century.) Over four hundred sheep were lost at Ewart.

The lake extended up the Glen valley to Kirknewton. During the evening of

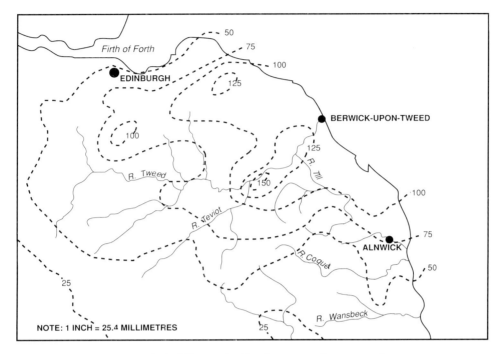

Fig 8.4 Rainfall over the Borders on 12 August 1948.

12 August the College burn at West Newton cut through its right bank and took a new route through Kirknewton flooding many houses. The post office was awash and next door the water was running through the windows. Great shoals of sand and gravel were spread across riverside fields covering crops to a depth of several feet. New gravel deposits in the river bed raised the water level. Road and rail from Kirknewton up the Bowmont valley were impassable. The road from Milfield to Lanton was torn up and the bridge from Westnewton to Crookhouse collapsed early on the 13th.

In Happy valley above Wooler, a bridge completely disappeared and another at Earle mill was left high and dry when the river took a new course. In Wooler, the Iron bridge first began to list and finally collapsed (Plates 8.3 and 8.4). With it went the gas, electricity and water services carried by the bridge to Weetwood Avenue. Just below the wrecked bridge an ex-War Department hut was torn from its foundations and destroyed just minutes after the occupants had abandoned it. The bowling green was covered to three feet and Station Road to two feet.

The Breamish overflowed at Brandon and flooded Powburn village for the third time in three years. A steel bridge on the Wooler/Chatton road shifted. Below the Wooler Water confluence, the Till bridge at Doddington became cracked and unsafe for use. A replacement bailey bridge was built in eleven hours on 30 August by sixty men from the School of Military Engineering and

165

Plate 8.3 The Iron bridge, Wooler during and after the flood

Plate 8.4 of 12 August 1948. *Photo*. Newcastle Chronicle.

remained in use for several decades in spite of the comment from the Commanding Officer, Major Ford:

They are all administrative workers, most of whom have never helped to build a bridge before and some are National Service recruits.

The large storage of water in Milfield plain delayed the passage of the flood downstream. With some foresight, workers at Heatherslaw mill near Ford moved five hundred bags of corn, each weighing sixteen stone, from the ground to a higher floor, using a hoist powered by the mill wheel, before the water rose sufficiently to submerge the undershot wheel. At its peak, the flood was four-and-a-half feet above the ground floor level and the flood level is still shown by a plaque in the visitor centre. The adjacent bridge deck was submerged and one foolhardy worker is reported to have made his way home along the bridge parapet. Further downstream, houses were affected at Twizel mill (to four feet) and Twizel bridge, boathouse and station.

Nearby, on the Tweed, streets in both Coldstream and Norham were under water and a canoe was used in Market Square at Coldstream. Seven people were rescued from the Boat House at Norham, when the water nearly reached roof level.

The whole coastal plain was awash, with every burn overflowing its banks. The only fatality reported was at Belford where Mrs Nellie Hall died from the shock of seeing her kitchen flooded. West Road, Belford, was flooded to a depth of four feet. Two bridges failed at Beal, where the sluice overtopped, and nearby, at Fenwick granary, part of the farm buildings was washed away and all the cottages were flooded. Cottages and the school were also flooded at Lucker from the Waren burn. Dicks Oldwalls dam failed near Middleton (Chapter 10) and the dam at Doxford Hall was overtopped. *Berwick Journal* reported the sighting near Seahouses of an 'elephants trunk', presumably a water-bearing tornado or waterspout, a destructive but fortunately rare phenomenon in Britain[13].

North of the Border, there were similar scenes of desolation. A railway engineer reported that fifteen bridges had completely disappeared and a larger number was damaged. The army was called in to assist in their reconstruction.

A national fund was launched by the Lord Provost of Edinburgh to relieve the distress of flood victims on both sides of the Border. King George VI and Queen Elizabeth made the first contributions. Help arrived from distant and unexpected sources. A gift of three cases of meat and two of dripping was made to victims in Norham and Islandshire by residents of Melbourne, Australia.

The run of poor weather had not yet ended, for another storm struck the following year on 25 October. The rainfall was not nearly as widespread as in August 1948 but on the Wooler Water and parts of the Breamish conditions were even worse. The centre of this storm appears to have been over the Cheviot where a daily rainfall of 123 mm accompanied by an easterly gale was recorded at Linhope. On lower land, totals generally ranged from 60 to 75 mm.

Most of the properties at Wooler flooded the previous year were again affected but there were additional problems at Haugh Head where the Wooler

Water breached the railway embankment at Surrey House and flowed along the main road to Wooler. The railway line lay slumped in the river bed for a distance of two hundred yards (Plate 8.5). Sixty people housed in Nissen huts along the roadside had to be evacuated, many of them sheltering in Smart's garage nearby. The experience of Mrs Mills was typical. She heard a knock and opened the door only to allow in a rush of water. The knock had been a tree trunk against the end of the house. She went to seek assistance across a small stream at the edge of her garden. Unaware that the wooden bridge had been washed away, she stepped into six feet of water and was rescued by a passing police officer.

Because of the serious damage to the railway at Haugh Head and the collapse of a railway bridge over the Lil burn at Ilderton, it was decided not to carry out repairs but to work trains for freight only, in two parts, from Alnwick to Ilderton and from Coldstream to Wooler. However, this arrangement was never viable and the southern stretch closed in March 1953 whilst the line north from Wooler struggled on until closure in 1965.

Roadways suffered in the upper reaches. On the Harthope burn, a mile of road was reported washed away in addition to all the bridges. Along the upper Breamish, the road from Ingram to Linhope was completely washed out for a quarter mile and farms were inaccessible to vehicles for several weeks.

In many places along the Breamish and Glen the banks were breached again but, at Kirknewton, the new bank protection with wire gabion crates prevented a recurrence of the damage of August 1948.

RIVER WORKS AND RECENT FLOODS

Just before the Border floods, a land drainage scheme had been prepared to improve the channel carrying capacity of the Glen and Till and to strengthen and construct new floodbanks. Channel work had only just begun at Ford when the August 1948 flood struck. The scheme was revised and, over the next six years, £110,000 was spent as part of the River Till Improvement Scheme. Flood banks were constructed or reconstructed, especially around the Milfield plain but also as far upstream as Ingram[11].

In spite of these works, floodbanks were overtopped and locally breached again on 28 August 1956. The flood was on a smaller scale but still affected several hundred hectares[14]. Recognising the impracticality of protecting all agricultural land against the recurrence of such events, it was thought better to reduce losses by building six large sluices through the banks at Fenton and Ewart to allow the controlled return of trapped surface water once the river level had receded.

Breakwaters and other training works were built at Powburn and Ingram in 1951 to maintain the channel in a fixed position and to alleviate the flooding at Powburn. In 1953, the building of relief flood arches at Redscar Bridge near Milfield was started and the river Till was widened for over a hundred metres upstream from the bridge.

On the Wooler water, apart from channel realignment and embanking, works included the construction of gabion weirs in an attempt to arrest vertical erosion

Plate 8.5 The slumped railway line at Haugh Head where the Wooler Water took a new course.

of the bed. The work was jeopardised for another two decades by the continuation of gravel extraction from the river.

On the small coastal streams, the channel of the Waren burn was widened and a floodbank was constructed in 1949 to reduce flood risk to Lucker village. More recently (1973-6) works have been carried out on North and South Lows to protect against both tidal and river flooding.

The river Coquet escaped the worst of the later Border floods but Rothbury racecourse and the road to Weldon Bridge were regularly flooded through the 1950s (Plate 8.6). During that decade the most severe flood was on 28 August 1956 when the two lowest houses at Rothbury Riverside were inundated to a depth of nearly a metre. At Thropton, where the Wreigh burn backed up, two cottages next to the bridge were flooded.

The Coquet shared with the Wansbeck the exceptional snowmelt flooding of March 1963, after a prolonged and snowy winter. The flood gathered strength in the lower reaches and, in addition to the usual affected houses in Rothbury, a home at the Stanners in Warkworth was flooded for the first time since 1900.

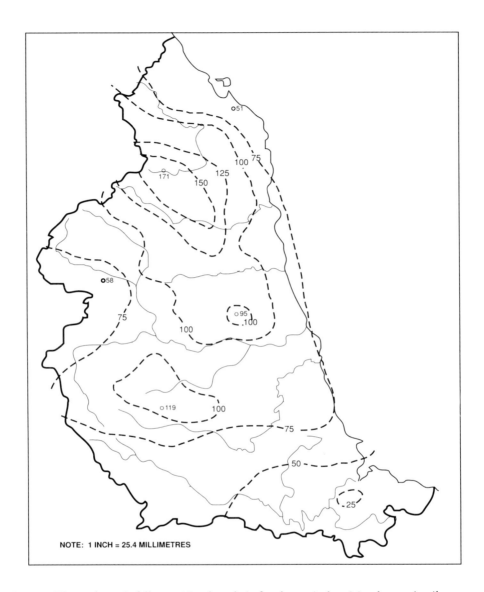

NOTE: 1 INCH = 25.4 MILLIMETRES

Fig 8.5 Three-day rainfall over Northumbria for the period 30 March to 1 April 1992.

A seventy-five-year-old woman there was forced to escape through a back window when water flowed through the front door.

Little flooding was experienced in the late 1960s or early 1970s but the period from 1978 to 1986 saw renewed flooding of agricultural land on the Coquet and Till on 24 December 1978, 28 March 1979, 2 March 1981, 3 January 1982, 4 February 1984 and 3 November 1984. The flood of 3 January 1982 was the highest on the Coquet since 1963 and affected four, rather than just the lowest

Plate 8.6 Rothbury race-course, now the Golf Course, was severely flooded on 28 August 1956.

two, houses at Rothbury Riverside. A floodbank scheme, just for these houses, was subsequently prepared by Northumbrian Water and completed in 1985. It held back the floods of 26 August 1986 which would otherwise have reached the lower two houses. On that occasion the swollen waters of the River Bowmont claimed the life of an agricultural researcher, Dr Robin Armstrong, when his Land Rover was swept into the river.

Whilst I was preparing this chapter in early 1992, a storm of unusual severity and extent struck the north of Northumberland. The rainfall and flooding were caused by a very slow moving weather system which tracked northwards over the area on 30 and 31 March and returned southwards on 1 April after a brief lull in the rainfall. Associated winds were from the north-east and consequently the heaviest rainfall was experienced on hills directly exposed to these winds, especially the eastern side of the Cheviots where a maximum three-day total of 171 mm was recorded in the upper Breamish catchment (Fig 8.5). Rainfall declined southward and towards the Pennines. The most notable feature of the storm was its duration, with precipitation continuing at some places for sixty hours.

River levels in the lower Coquet reached their highest levels for over a hundred years and on the Aln and Till the worst conditions were experienced since the Border floods of the later 1940s. On the river Coquet water leaked through the floodbank at Rothbury Riverside and entered the lowest house. The National Rivers Authority pumped to keep the levels down and managed to save the other three houses. The river crossed the main road at the Alms Houses and residents were evacuated as a precautionary measure. Downstream from

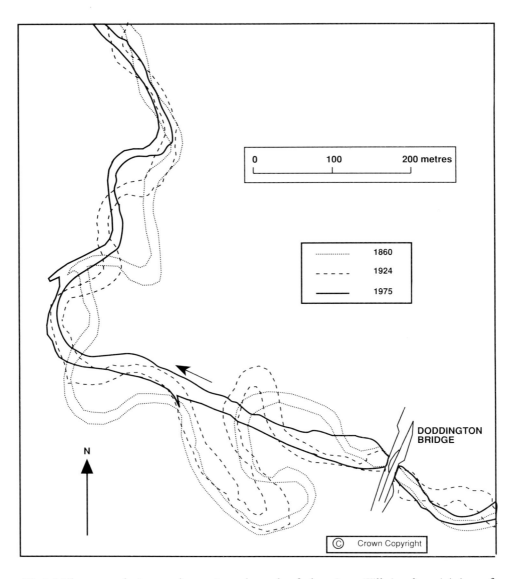

Fig 8.6 The meandering and moving channel of the river Till in the vicinity of Doddington bridge.

Brinkburn to Warkworth the main sufferers were at mill properties. Brinkburn mill, in the process of refurbishment, was flooded to a depth of a metre; Weldon mill was surrounded and four recently converted houses at Felton mill had lower floors covered to a depth of up to 1.5 metres. Two houses at the former Warkworth mill were flooded for the first time this century. Flood marks there, and at the nearby Hermitage, a medieval chapel carved in the cliff face, overlooking the Coquet, enable comparisons to be made with earlier floods. The April 1992 flood was 0.31 metres higher than in 1963 and 0.21 metres higher than in 1900, but 0.72 metres lower than in February 1831.

Norman Gray, a pensioner living at the Stanners, Warkworth, had his house flooded for only the second time in his life. It was a few inches deep on the floor in 1963 but this time it reached the mantelpiece. He watched the river rise during the afternoon, surrounding the riverbank picnic table. He was expecting the level to fall back after high tide at 3.30 p.m. but the river continued to rise for several hours. The water backed up the drains and into the bathroom and, as he went to inspect, the door burst open and water surged into his living room, extinguishing his open fire in a billow of steam. Like his mother thirty years before, he escaped through the back window.

Although the level was high on the river Aln, no houses were affected but three bridges in Hulne Park were reported severely damaged.

Along the Till and its tributaries, extensive areas of agricultural land were flooded as banks were breached or overtopped. However, only three properties were affected, all mills, at Canno and Lanton on the Glen near Kirknewton, and at Heatherslaw mill, Ford. There the manager of the Visitor Centre again used the mill wheel to hoist bags of corn from the mill floor before the mill water reached them.

MOVING RIVERS

The rivers of the Cheviots are predominantly alluvial streams: they have beds and banks of erodable material. In the upper reaches, and especially on the Wooler Water and College burn, the material is predominantly cobbles and boulders whereas in the middle and lower reaches, for example on the Till, the bed material is mainly sand.

Alluvial rivers are subject to gradual changes of the kind described in elementary geography textbooks, for example erosion on the outer bends of meanders, accretion on inner bends and the eventual cutting-off of the meander and creation of oxbow lakes[15,16]. Even over a decade, such gradual changes may be imperceptible. However, surveys of the Till made by comparing maps show that there has been lateral movement between 1860 and 1975 of up to four channel widths[17]. Figure 8.6 shows an example of the moving channel in the vicinity of Doddington bridge.

Such changes may occur without any appreciable alteration in the shape, slope or appearance of the channel: in spite of episodic erosion and deposition they maintain a quasi-equilibrium with the controlling flow in the channel. In the case of the Till, a survey by Blogg[17] showed only a nine per cent decrease in the sinuosity and amplitude of meanders over the period of study.

In other instances, channel changes have been more rapid, and have involved significant vertical and horizontal movement of the channel bed as well as changes in form, for example from a meandering to a braided river with a dividing channel and creation of islands. Such changes may result from human activities in the river or over the contributing catchment, or from an exceptional flood. In the case of the Wooler Water, these conditions appear to have combined to create channel instability which has persisted for several decades. Without doubt gravel extraction from the river bed to provide a cheap source of aggregate for construction has accelerated channel change. One such site near Earle mill just upstream from Wooler was worked from the late 1930s. Gravel extraction destroys the armouring layer, which tends to develop on the bed during periods of comparative stability as boulders and pebbles settle and interlock. With this protection gone, erosion and transport of boulders can be initiated at much lower velocities. The irregular redistribution of bed material also creates turbulence and rapid variations in velocity. Thus gravel disturbance provides both the means (higher velocity) and the conditions (lower bed resistance) for instability.

The second major contributing cause was, of course, the series of floods, culminating in the flood of October 1949 which dramatically changed the channel. In the upper reaches, many changes occurred without any significant earlier channel works but the effect was greatest at Earle mill near where the railway embankment was breached. Riverside trees were stripped away and the Northumberland Catchment Board reported that the river had formed new channels and trebled its width, leaving fields strewn with boulders and gravel. The amount of erosion was greater than after the flood in 1948 and five large bulldozers were occupied for three months in channel restoration.

Whether this latter work had any significant benefit is difficult to establish from a perspective of forty years, but it is clear that the channel has not stabilised and that rapid incision of the river into its gravel bed has moved upstream aided by gravel workings which continued on a reduced scale until 1973. Remnants of the old river bed with bank protection works can now be seen some eight metres above the present bed level and Plate 8.7 shows how the originally low footbridge at Haugh Head was undermined and is now left with an extended pier high above the new channel.

These prolonged channel readjustments demonstrate the sensitivity which is now required of the National Rivers Authority in its own operations in gravel bed rivers and in controlling actions by developers. The primary need is to protect land and property from excessive and frequent inundation but the requirements are sometimes conflicting or even irreconcileable. Gravel, recently accumulated in the bed, which is causing obstructions to flow and raising water levels, may have to be removed, but its removal may create weaknesses in bed and banks and make them more vulnerable to erosion.

There is also increasing recognition of the need to encourage the conservation of aquatic and riverbank habitats and to maintain species diversity and numbers. However, excessive aquatic vegetation may impede flows and encourage sedimentation. The object, therefore, is to carry out works which will maintain

Plate 8.7 The Wooler Water has cut into its gravel bed and undermined the footbridge at Haugh Head. At this bridge the original bed was at the level of the ledge on the pier. Downstream the river cut much deeper. *Photo D. Archer 1990.*

the carrying capacity of the channel whilst minimising the associated disturbance. This is usually done by working from one bank only and preserving features of visual interest such as trees and shrubs whose roots also protect the bank.

REFERENCES

1. Robson, D. A. 'A guide to the geology of the Cheviot Hills', *Trans. The Natural History Society of Northumbria*, vol. 43, no 1 (1981)
2. Robson, D. A. *The geology of northeast England*. The Natural History Society of Northumbria, Special Publication, (1981)
3. Riley, H. T. (ed. and trans.) *Annals of Roger De Hoveden, comprising the History of England and of other Countries of Europe from 732 to 1201 AD*, (London, 1853)
4. Maxwell, H. (trans.) *The Chronicle of Lanercost*, (Glasgow, 1913)
5. Tate, G. *History of the Borough, Castle and Barony of Alnwick*, (1866)
6. Dixon, D. D. *Upper Coquetdale, Northumberland, its History, Traditions, Folklore and Scenery*, (Newcastle upon Tyne, 1903)
7. Delaval-Ford Papers at Northumberland Record Office
8. Dickens, T. *The River Bridges of Northumberland*: vol. 1 The River Till and its tributaries; vol. 2 The Aln; vol 3 The Coquet, Pelaw
9. McEwan, L. J. 'The establishment of an historical flood chronology for the River Tweed

catchment, Berwickshire, Scotland', *Scottish Geographical Magazine*, 106 (1990)

10. Anon. 'Heavy rainfall in Durham and Northumberland on October 26th 1900', *Symon's Monthly Meteorological Magazine*, 418 (1900)
11. Northumberland Rivers and Catchment Board. Report 1945-50.
12. Glasspole, J. and Douglas, C. K. M. 'Tweed valley floods, Heavy rainfall of August 11-12th 1948', *Meteorological Magazine*, 78 (1949)
13. Gordon, A. H. 'Waterspouts', *Weather*, 6 (1951)
14. Common, R. 'The Border floods, August 1956, observations and comments', *Scottish Geographical Magazine*, 72 (1958)
15. Hooke, J. M. and Redmond C. E. 'River channel changes in England and Wales', *Journ Inst. Water and Environmental Management*, 3, no 4 (1989)
16. Milne, J. A. 'River channel change in the Harthope valley, Northumberland since 1897', University of Newcastle upon Tyne. *Dept of Geography Res. Series*, no 13 (1982)
17. Blogg, G. 'Channel changes on the River Till Northumbria since 1860', BSc Dissertation, Portsmouth Polytechnic, (1990)

9. FLASH FLOOD!

Through thick vapour swaddle
Violet lightning shakes its shutters
And thunder trundles its drums from the highest attic
Of heaven to the lowest, furthest basement.
                    Ted Hughes   *He Gets up at Dark Dawn*   *Season Songs*

Flash floods are not usually associated with Britain. The words conjure up a picture of a sudden deluge in the desert and the resulting torrent of water mud and rocks surging down a normally dry wadi, eroding its bed and eventually spreading its load on an alluvial plain. But remove the words 'desert' and 'dry wadi' and we have a description of a phenomenon which is not at all uncommon in the British Isles.

Perhaps the best-known flash flood in Britain is that which occurred at Lynmouth in North Devon on 15 August 1952. On that tragic night 34 people were killed, 93 buildings destroyed or subsequently demolished, 28 bridges succumbed and 132 vehicles were destroyed[1]. In one day 229 mm of rain fell over Exmoor in the headwaters of the river Lyn but, more significantly, there was a period during the early evening when the rain fell at a rate of 125 mm per hour. The resulting flood wave gathered strength, especially over the last kilometre of the East and West Lyn tributaries where the channels drop a hundred metres to the sea and converge within the village. A wall of water, said to be forty feet high, crashed down on the unsuspecting village. Trees, telegraph poles and ten-ton boulders acted as battering rams against the puny walls of houses, or cut away the foundations from beneath. It is estimated that, at its peak, the flow of water through the village was 650 cubic metres (or tonnes) per second from a catchment area of 101 square kilometres[2].

The storms which cause flash floods such as the one at Lynmouth differ in two ways from those described in the previous chapters. They often cover no more than a few square kilometres, with devastating impact on small tributaries but little effect on the main river. Unlike the more widespread floods associated with frontal conditions, these intense localised storms are of short duration although they may occur within a longer period of more steady rainfall. They are convectional in type.

It is interesting to compare the heaviest rainfall in Britain[3] with the highest measured totals in Northumbria (Table 9.1). Comparisons are usually made between daily totals, since it is in this form that data are most commonly collected, although some high daily totals also include moderate rainfall in upland areas occurring over the whole day.

Table 9.1 Highest daily rainfall (millimetres), 1865-1975.
Note that 100 mm approximately equals 4 inches.

A. Britain   B. Northumbria.

County/Catchment	Station	Date			Fall mm
A. Britain					
Dorset	Martinstown	18	July	1955	279
Somerset	Bruton	28	June	1917	243
Somerset	Cannington	18	Aug.	1924	239
Devon	Longstone Barrow	15	Aug.	1955	229
Glamorgan	Llust Wen Resvr.	11	Nov.	1929	211
Highland	Loch Quoich	11	Oct.	1916	208
Cumbria	Seathwaite	12	Nov.	1897	204
Cornwall	Camelford	8	June	1957	203
B. Northumbria					
Wansbeck	Angerton	7	Sep.	1898	170
Leven	Kildale	11	Sep.	1976	145
Leven	Kildale	4	Sep.	1931	126
Till	Linhope	25	Oct.	1949	122
Till	Yetholm	12	Aug.	1948	119
Leven	Kildale	22	July	1930	116
Tyne	Newcastle	22	June	1941	113
Wansbeck	Sweethope Lough	29	Aug.	1975	108

(Note: World maxima of daily rainfall are on quite a different scale: 1870 mm was recorded at La Reunion in the Indian Ocean during a tropical cyclone in 1952.)

It can be seen from this table that Northumbria lags far behind the country as a whole, and especially south-west England, in terms of its maximum daily fall. A national study by Bleasdale[4] identified 142 occasions when more than 125 mm and over 450 occasions when 100 mm occurred in the day for the years 1893 to 1960. Only one and eight, respectively, of these occasions were in Northumbria.

Comparisons of rainfall over shorter durations are less certain but Jackson prepared a list in 1974 of the top fifty two-hour totals in Britain[5]. This included only one from the north-east: a storm at Newcastle in 1941. However, some Northumbrian storms were omitted from the list and a comparison is made in Table 9.2. The totals for the Northumbrian stations are for the full storm duration shown.

Table 9.2 Highest recorded rainfall (millimetres) over short durations.

A. Britain   B. Northumbria

County/Catchment Station		Date			Fall mm	Duration hrs
A. Britain						
Yorkshire	Hewenden Resvr	11	June	1956	155	2
Kent	Sevenoaks	5	Sep.	1958	131	
Somerset	Cannington	16	Aug.	1924	127	
Lincs	Cranwell	11	July	1932	126	
Cornwall	Camelford	8	June	1957	124	
Anglesey	Llansadwrn	10	Aug.	1957	124	
Kent	Bromley	22	July	1934	118	
Dorset	Martinstown	18	July	1955	117	
B. Northumbria						
Wansbeck	Angerton	7	Sep.	1898	170	3
Tyne	Newcastle	22	June	1941	113	2h 20m
Wear	Ireshopeburn	17	July	1983	105	2h 30m

Although the Angerton storm ranks with the highest two-hour intensities in Britain, the rainfall data suggest that severe short-period storms also appear to be less frequent in Northumbria. Nevertheless, the incidence of flash flooding suggests that the available rainfall information greatly underestimates the frequency and severity of such events. Storms often occur where there are no raingauges or gauges measure lesser amounts on the fringe of the storm. The gauging network is not sufficiently dense (144 daily gauges over a total area of 9207 square kilometres in 1992). Indeed, with changes in the location of gauges, if there were a recurrence of the Angerton storm in 1992, no daily measurement would exceed 50 mm. Most of the floods described later have no associated rainfall data.

Some of the largest or most interesting floods are described here and a chronological summary is given at the end of the chapter.

NORTHUMBRIA'S GREATEST RAINFALL
– ANGERTON 7 SEPTEMBER 1898
An account of the storm is given in detail in *Symon's British Rainfall* for the year, based on the reports of individual observers and a the County Highway Surveyor[6]. It is clear that the storm was exceptional over a very small area, stretching from Bolam to Netherwitton in the middle reaches of the Wansbeck catchment. Apart from the record 170 mm at Angerton, exceptional totals were also recorded at Gallowhill three kilometres south (121 mm) and Netherwitton

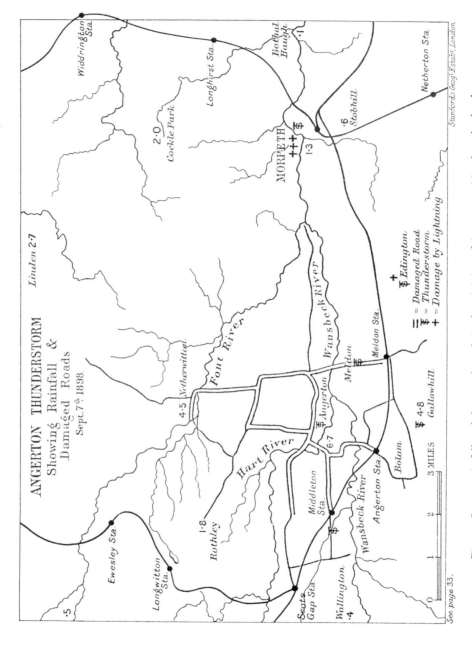

Fig 9.1 Storm rainfall and damaged roads in the vicinity of Angerton, Northumberland 7 September 1898. (From British Rainfall, 1898.)

4.5 kilometres north (113 mm). Only two other totals exceeded 50mm. At Wallington, six kilometres to the west, only 11 mm was recorded. The observer there noted that two fields away there was no rain at all and men continued haymaking all day.

The rain started around midday and was accompanied by severe thunder and hail said to be one-and-a-half inches in diameter at Bolam. Glasshouses and roof lights were much damaged. Lightning set farm buildings alight at Edlington and Wansbeck House in Morpeth, and animals were reported struck dead as far away as Ebchester and Felton.

Fig 9.1 shows damaged roads as indicated by the Highway Surveyor. In the Meldon, Hartburn and Angerton areas, some roads were excavated to a depth of four or five feet and in one recently remetalled place a channel three feet deep and two feet wide was cut down the centre of the road. 'No roadman with pick and shovel could have made one so uniform. Anyone seeing the roads the morning after the rain would have thought they were the beds of dried-up streams, and it took three or four months labour to reinstate them.'

Tributary burns filled culverts and destroyed walls and fences with unprecedented ferocity. Eighteen footbridges were washed away. The Wansbeck rose remarkably quickly, reaching a peak in Morpeth by 6 p.m. and flooding houses in the Stanners, whilst at Sheepwash the observer reported that 'the River Wansbeck rose 8 or 9 feet in an incredibly short time. The great rush of water brought down scores of sheaves of corn, pikes of hay, young trees, boats, sheep, pigs and goats.'

A MODERN PEAT SLIDE IRESHOPEBURN – 17 JULY 1983

The storm of 17 July 1983 and the resulting peat slides and flash floods are probably the best documented of any such event in Britain, with descriptions and analysis of mechanisms in three research papers by Paul Carling and his colleagues[7,8,9].

The summer of 1983 started wet, with well above average rainfall in May, but the months of June and July were predominantly dry though punctuated by localised intense storms including 80 mm in two hours at West Woodburn (Redesdale) on 12 July and over Killhope Moor on 23 July, where there were no gauges to measure the rainfall intensity. But the most exceptional storm occurred on 17 July at Noon Hill, on the divide between the Ireshope burn and West Grain tributaries of the Wear, and Langdon beck, a tributary of the Tees. Simultaneously, an intense convectional cell developed over the headwaters of the West Allen.

A recording gauge at Burnhope reservoir (Fig 9.2) registered the start of the storm at precisely 3.24 p.m., but failed after a few minutes probably because of a lightning strike. The adjacent daily gauge registered 87 mm. At Ireshope Plains, a little to the east, 104.8 mm fell between 3.30 and 6 p.m., the observer stating that the greater part fell in the core period from 3.45 to 5 p.m. and that the storm seemed even more intense over the moors to the south.

His observation seems vindicated by the devastation of the headwater moorland. Masses of peat gave way at five locations and moved bodily down

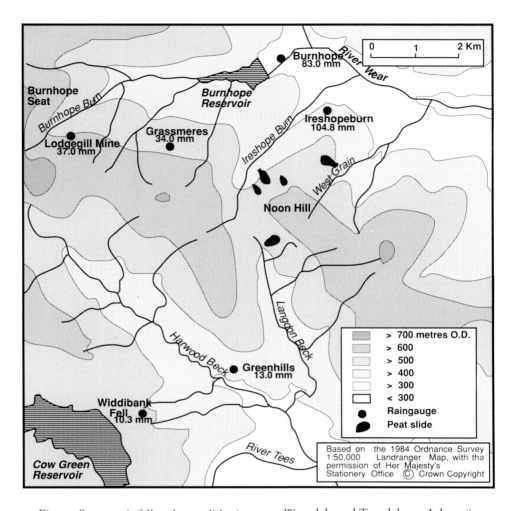

Fig 9.2 Storm rainfall and peat slides in upper Weardale and Teesdale, 17 July 1983.

the hillsides, three towards the Ireshope burn and one each toward the West Grain and Langdon beck. In the two largest, areas of 2.5 hectares were left completely bare and grooved where previously the peat had been one to two metres deep (Plate 9.1). Carling has estimated that, in each of these cases, over 30,000 tons of material had been set in motion. As it moved off downslope the peat cracked into a chaotic jumble of large blocks and was thrust over adjacent undisturbed peat. In one case the main slip was nearly five hundred metres long. Some peat blocks were carried into the swollen becks and rolled into spindle shapes up to two metres in diameter.

The storm initiated flood flows, exceptional in their peak discharges, the rate of rise in water level and the size of boulders transported. Conditions were most extreme in the smallest catchment, the West Grain. On this stream there is an offtake structure with associated weir and recorder house at NY 872469 to divert the headwater flow to Burnhope reservoir. The flood wave overtopped the recorder house and removed its slate roof. A large boulder was projected through the wooden shutters and was found pinioning the remains of the water level recorder on the floor. Alongside the hut was a boulder jam with the largest block more than a metre in diameter. A short distance downstream the road culvert was surcharged; the water backed up and flowed over the road. The catchment area to this point is only 1.86 square kilometres and Carling has estimated the peak discharge from culvert geometry as 22 cubic metres per second, and 16 cubic metres per second from the size of boulders transported. This ranks with the highest flow per unit area reliably recorded anywhere in the British Isles[10].

On the Langdon beck the occupants of Valence Lodge were brought from the house by the sound of the approaching flood wave and described the flow as 'a wall of mud with the appearance and consistency of chocolate sauce'. Langdon Common bridge was again overtopped and the black 'sauce' poured over the road (Plate 9.2). The estimated discharge at this point of 29 cubic metres per second is not exceptional but Carling shows that this flow was almost entirely generated in the small headwater catchment of 3.5 square kilometres.

Ireshope burn discharges into the river Wear at the village of the same name. Near the confluence is a small caravan park in an idyllic setting on the river's edge. The wave front picked up the caravan (fortunately unoccupied) nearest the burn and carried it off into the river Wear. Another with a terrified family inside was set afloat but saved from destruction by being held against a wall. There was no time for escape.

Hydrologists in Britain, and especially those accustomed to lowland rivers, are inclined to dismiss as exaggeration descriptions of flood waves as 'a wall of water'. In most floods generated by longer periods of rain or thaw, even where the rise is said to be rapid, the slope of the water surface is not evident. I must admit to having been amongst the doubters. In this case the unanimous descriptions of observers were supported by the record at gauging stations on the Wear and West Allen. At these stations, water level and discharge are recorded at fifteen minute intervals in stilling wells adjacent to the river (Table 9.3). Allowing for the delay in filling the well from the river, the change in level between successive measurements implies a near vertical wave front one-and-a-half metres high. This was confirmed by a young visitor from Washington, swimming in the West Allen, who barely escaped with his life. The peak flows in the main rivers were by no means exceptional.

Plate 9.1 Peat slide near Ireshopeburn caused by the storm of 17 July 1983. Photographed the following winter. *Photo. D. Archer.*

Plate 9.2 The Langdon beck in spate with 'the appearance and consistency of chocolate sauce' as it joins the Harwood beck, 17 July 1983. Note that the Harwood beck (right) is almost unaffected.

Table 9.3 Flow and level statistics for the flash flood of 17 July 1983.

River	Location	Peak Flow	Max. 15 min rise	Total rise	Time of rise	Max. 15 min fall	Time of Fall
		m³/sec	m	m	p.m.	m	p.m.
Wear	Stanhope	94	1.54	1.83	5.15	0.15	6.15
Wear	Witton Pk	77	1.30	1.66	8.00	0.10	9.00
W. Allen	Hindley Wrae	67	1.51	1.51	5.00	0.14	5.45

There was one further result of the peat slide. The high load of solids in suspension and altered water chemistry caused a massive fish kill, especially in the river Tees. More than 7,500 fish were estimated to have died. Even at Darlington, seventy kilometres downstream, the fish monitors used to detect pollutants entering the treatment works at Broken Scar died when the flood wave reached there at 9 a.m. on 18 July. The pumps were immediately switched off.

ANCIENT PEAT SLIDES
The peat slide at Ireshopeburn was unusual but a search of historical records shows it was by no means unique. The earliest record is provided by the diary of Christopher Sanderson[11] for 1678 which briefly describes a storm on 3 July in Eggleston, Lunedale and Balderdale which 'carried away grounds'. Another description, perhaps of the same event but assigned to 1689, is given by Camden in *Britannia*, published in 1722[12]:

. . . about midsummer there happened an Eruption of Water of the Mosses; and the earth which was broken thereby, is computed to be about 150 yards long and in some places 3 and in others 3 score yards broad and about 6 or 7 deep. Which great quantity of Earth being most of it carried by the flood of water into the neighbouring brook and so into the River Bauder, did great damage by overflowing the Meadows and leaving behind it vast quantities of Mud. . . . It poisoned all the fish not only in the aforesaid Brook and the Bauder but also in the Tees for many miles.

Still within the Tees catchment, where the Lodgegill Syke drains the eastern slopes of Meldon Hill towards the Tees above Cow Green reservoir, the first geological surveyors located a peat slide in 1870, of recent but uncertain date. The scar at the head of the slide and eroded peat blocks are still visible.

Just five hundred metres away two other slides occurred on 6 July 1963[13]. Both are about 230 metres long and 36 metres across at their widest point, tapering below and becoming gullies which fall into the Lodgegill Syke. Scientists from the nearby Moorhouse field station were quickly on the spot to examine the site. They estimated about six thousand cubic metres of peat had been removed. Again the convectional storm was extremely localised. The nearest raingauge at Moorhouse, 3.5 kilometres to the north-west, recorded only 11 mm. Peak flows in the Tees were unexceptional though the pollutant cloud the next day caused the treatment works to stop abstraction for seven hours.

Peat slides in the north-east are not confined to the higher Pennines. A similar incident is recorded in the Cheviot hills on the flanks of Bloodybush Edge which divides the waters of the Usway burn and Alwin, flowing to the Coquet, from the headwaters of the river Breamish flowing east towards Ingram. The event was the focus of that year's *British Rainfall* (1893) which published extracts from local Alnwick newspapers and a report and photographs by Jevon J. Muschamp Perry, the Vicar of St Paul's, Alnwick, on the 'fall of a waterspout on the Cheviot Range':

On July 2nd 1893 the weather became oppressive and sultry; about 10.00 a.m. the clouds became very large and seemed to come from three different quarters and meet over the east side of Bloodybush Edge with a swirling motion. About 1 p.m. the cloud broke. The principal fall occurred within the watershed of the Breamish which on this occasion swept away its bridges and destroyed long stretches of the road. It came down with a suddenness and power for which neither the memory of the oldest inhabitant nor the rumour of past tradition could find any parallel. The flood in the Breamish came down like a wall and rose and fell again in the space of an hour and a half.

The Breamish is reported to have risen forty feet in thirty minutes and two bridges at Ingram were carried away. At Low Bleakhope, the nearest habitation 2.5 kilometres to the east of the peat slide, a rainfall total was estimated from a previously empty bucket exposed to the rain which was found to contain fifteen inches of water. Making allowance for the taper of the sides this could hardly represent less than 200 mm of rainfall.

The main peat slide was on the eastern flank of Bloodybush Edge with a smaller slide draining north to the Clay burn and hence to the Usway burn and Coquet. J. J. M. Perry continues:

For a space of at least 30 or 40 acres the upper peat has been ploughed to a depth of some 5 feet and the moor bed beneath laid bare. Enormous masses of this dark peaty soil have been hurled right and left, piled one on top of another and a vast quantity of blocks of earth have been carried hundreds of yards down the hill so as to present the appearance of a broad stream of blocks.

When I first visited the site (Grid reference NT 907145) in April 1987 the arcuate headwall scar was clearly visible and etched out by the last of the winter snow. The area from which the peat was evacuated is predominantly grass covered and contrasts with the surrounding heather. Downhill hummocks of torn peat still stand more than one metre above the surrounding heather.

Floods were also spectacular on the Usway and Alwin. 'The Alwin came down in such force carrying sheep and weirs before it. The flood bore on to Harbottle, going down the Coquet like a moving wall.' The Coquet from Alwinton to Rothbury retained for several weeks the trace of the flood as a black watermark[14].

THE LYNMOUTH OF THE NORTH – BELLINGHAM 14 MAY 1911
The floods described above occurred on sparsely inhabited uplands and affected few properties. However, there are many accounts of local storms over tributary headwaters which have caused extensive damage. Burns, which

normally carry only a trickle through towns, have become raging torrents in Rothbury, Alnwick, Morpeth, Otterburn, Hexham and elsewhere. The most spectacular storm occurred in Bellingham on 14 May 1911.

The Hareshaw burn rises on the moorland of Corsenside Common and on its way to the Tyne tumbles over the picturesque Hareshaw Linn waterfall, and through an attractive wooded glen before passing through Bellingham to the North Tyne. On the day in question there was a 'terrific downpour of hail followed by rain in sheets lasting for two hours'. The burn rose to a height of from ten to fifteen feet and almost every building abutting its banks was wrecked. The storm is well recorded by a daring photographer, both during and after the event, and the photographs now form a part of the Blankenbergs collection housed in the Northumberland Record Office. They speak for themselves (Plates 9.3, 9.4, 9.5): the missing sidewalls, collapsing ceilings, hanging fireplaces, projecting beams and the forlorn and disbelieving residents. Fortunately no lives were lost.

Hareshaw Drift colliery was flooded but the two ironworks dams at the head of the town remarkably survived (though the lower dam failed in a flood in September 1968). Through the town all outbuildings, whether wood or brick and mortar, were swept away. Sewage pipes and gas mains crossing the burn were torn up and footbridges carried away. A boulder apparently about three tons in weight was carried several hundred metres downstream.

All around the dry weather of the early summer continued with low river levels. Even the Rede and the North Tyne above Bellingham rose little above normal.

LIGHTNING AND RAILWAY BRIDGE FAILURE
– FOURSTONES 5 JULY 1852

Death by lightning seems nowadays a fairly unusual occurrence, but several storms in the middle of the nineteenth century produced many fatalities. It is not clear whether the change is due to the greater protection now afforded by houses or by the change in the character of storms.

The thunderstorms of 7 July 1852 seem to have developed in widely separated cells. Eight people were struck dead at places as far apart as Alnwick and Weardale and two others died when a wall collapsed as water accumulated behind it at Gateshead. At Swinehope two people were killed while sitting in a bedroom[15].

John Grey of Dilston records the storm[16] in a graphic letter to his wife:

Such a fall of water for four miles square I have never heard of in this country. It came down so as to fill tubs standing outside in a minute. I went and found the colliery at Fourstones full of water run in at the mouth; nothing could resist it. Capon's Cleugh bridge and road which cost us 530 six years ago, all gone into the Tyne where it formed an island with trees washed down.

A workman was on the line at Allerwash Bridge at our mill; saw the water come up like an avalanche, stepped back and in a moment saw the railway bridge over the Allerwash Burn carried bodily into the Tyne and swept away in fragments.

A mile further west, the ruins of our Capon's Cleugh bridge came in a deluge of water and stones and trees against the railway. The culvert for the passing of the small burn was stopped; the train came up; the engine and tender got over but the line broke under the carriages. The guard fell through the bottom of his van, was swept in the flood of the burn across the Tyne and landed unhurt in our plantation on the south side!. How he escaped being crushed to death among the splinters and broken planks of the carriages I cannot conceive. It is a miraculous escape and he can tell little about it but that he thought he was to be drowned. It was the little red-faced man. No passengers were killed; seven were rather hurt.

Elsewhere, the flood carried away nearly a mile of the Spennymoor branch of the Clarence railway and damaged other lines near Ferryhill.

CITY STORMS

The city streets have not escaped either. The only north-east storm to reach Jackson's list of national two-hour storms[5] was at Newcastle on 22 June 1941. However, because of the war restrictions, the storm and its effects was not noted in the local papers. *British Rainfall* records that a succession of severe thunderstorms passed over Newcastle in the afternoon and, between 2.25 and 4.45 p.m., there was 113 mm of rain. Of this, 95 mm fell in eighty-five minutes. The location of the measurement is not stated but it would appear that the area of greatest intensity was west and north of the city centre from Gosforth to Denton burn. The drains were quite inadequate to carry such a volume and the

Plate 9.3 Flood water streaming through Bellingham during the flood of 14 May 1911.

Plate 9.4 Aftermath of the flood of 14 May 1911, J. Brown's warehouse Bellingham.

Plate 9.5 Brookside Place, Bellingham after the flood of 14 May 1911.

water flowed deep over roads and footpaths, scouring channels in the road and lifting pavement blocks and flooding many houses.

A book of photographs of the resulting flood damage, held by Newcastle City Library, shows dramatic evidence of the devastation on the normally placid Denton burn. The culvert under the A69, just west of the roundabout, was filled and water flooded out over the roadway (Plate 9.6). Downstream, the river eroded its bed nearly two metres deep and left garden sheds and fences hanging over the chasm or carried them away. Four further sites recorded rainfall of more than 60 mm in the day.

	mm
Newcastle (King's College)	62.7
Newcastle (Leazes Park)	64.2
Throckley Filters	65.9
Chopwellwood	77.7

As can be seen from the summary of events below, this is by no means the only occasion of an intense storm over Newcastle. Perhaps the most spectacular storm of the nineteenth century was that on 18 June 1839 which affected the city centre. To quote Latimer's Local Record[15]:

About four o'clock this afternoon a tremendous thunderstorm visited Newcastle. Rain continued to descend with the utmost fury for nearly two hours during which time the damage done was almost incredible. Upon the Leazes a great accumulation of water took place which overthrew several yards of a wall about two foot thick near the Leazes Lane. At Barras Bridge a great flood completely filled the kitchens of two houses and forced away the partition wall between them. The flood which rushed from Gallowgate and the Town Moor, down the Darn Crook, soon caused an immense lake in Newgate Street and completely closed the thoroughfare. Shops were flooded to a depth of several feet. In the Westgate the torrent rushed with prodigious force and several houses were deeply inundated.

The Sandhill was impassable for nearly two hours. Dean Street, The Side and the Butcher Bank were each the channel of a great stream and in the last named street a boy was carried away by the flood and caught with some difficulty at the corner of the Sandhill. At the Stockbridge the water was five feet in depth and the quantity of furniture, flour and bread etc destroyed in the houses, shops and warehouses was quite enormous.

At Tantobie a man and his wife named Teesdale and one of their children were killed by lightning while sitting in their house. At Byers Green a railway labourer was struck dead. Near Alnwick a pig was struck dead in a cart but driver and horse escaped harmless.

A PARADOX

In the vast majority of rainfall stations in Northumbria, the highest recorded daily rainfall is less than 60 mm even in those stations with records for a hundred years. Rodda[17,18], in a national study, estimated the rainfall likely to recur on average every fifty and one hundred years at a particular site and found that for

Plate 9.6 The West Road, Newcastle, under water at Denton Bankfoot, as the Denton burn overflowed on 22 June 1941. *Photo.* Newcastle Chronicle.

Northumbria the 50-year rainfall was around 65mm and the 100-year rainfall about 75mm.

On the other hand, the record shows that, somewhere in Northumbria, there are a couple of storms every decade whose destructive force suggests rainfalls far in excess of these figures.

The paradox can be resolved by considering the area over which such storms occur. Often the storm core appears to cover an area of less than ten square kilometres. Even if there were one of these events a year, the chance of one occurring in any year at a particular location or over a specified raingauge must be more than a thousand-to-one over the total Northumbrian area of 9207 square kilometres.

The chances of measuring that rainfall are also remote. There are 144 daily raingauges over the area or one per sixty-four square kilometres. Given a storm-centre area of ten square kilometres, there is a six-to-one chance that there is no raingauge in the area.

These are rough calculations based on assumptions of storm size and uniformity and an even spread of raingauges but they show how there is a risk of under-rating the maximum storm rainfall and flash flood that can occur over the region. This has important practical consequences for the design of dams and their spillways as is illustrated in the next chapter.

SUMMARY OF HISTORICAL FLASH FLOODS IN THE NORTHUMBRIAN AREA

1678 July 3 Eggleston, Lunedale and Balderdale. 'Carried away grounds.'

1728 May 12 Newburn. Carried off stable kilnhouse and mill and moved stones in burn weighing 2 tons. Overflowed the end of Newburn bridge.

1761 July 12 Rothbury. Thunderstorm 1 hour duration. Sand and stones thrown in heaps against houses. Houses flooded, roads rutted.

1766 July 21 Allendale. Violent thunderstorm. River rose almost instantly[19]. Boy carried 1/2 mile downstream but rescued. Also affected South Tyne where a woman was drowned.

1777 June ? Hexhamshire. Ground torn up. Houses flooded. Damage to stone walls and pavements.

1787 July 24 Walbottle/Newburn. Mill at Walbottle swept away and man drowned. Three houses destroyed at Newburn and three drowned. Pont also swollen.

1789 July 21 Hexham. Thunderstorm. Lower part of Hexham including two tan yards flooded.

1789 July 23 Chester-le-Street. Forge mill and skin mill at Bracken Hill destroyed. Houses flooded and bridge near Lumley Castle swept away.

1792 July 16 Otterburn. Thunderstorm in hills above Otterburn. Rain for 2 hours. 'Waterspout.' Rede rose 13 feet (1 foot higher than in 1771). Bridge and several mills carried away near Bellingham.

1792 Aug. 26 Newcastle/Gateshead. Damage at Stockbridge, Pandon, Blyths Nook. Flooding on Team/Derwent/Tyne. Rain 12 to 7 p.m.

1809 Aug. 12 Newcastle. Rain for 6 hours. Pandon burn overflowed. Bridge on Ouseburn at Woolsington carried away. Man drowned in Ouseburn.

1818 July 18 Otterburn. 'Waterspout at Davyshield common.' Most inhabitants of Otterburn affected. Water 8 inches over the counter at the grocer's.

1829 July 24 Haydon Bridge and Hexham. Thunderstorm 3 to 8 p.m. Langley burn swept away bridge at Langley Castle. Post Office at Haydon Bridge flooded[20]. Cockshaw Burn flooded houses at Cockshaw and Gilligate to base of windows. Damage to tanyards. Also at Hartside.

1832 Aug. 25 Barnard Castle. Road Barnard Castle to Bowes almost impassable.

1833 June 11 Newcastle. Thunderstorm 1 hour. Flooding of Newgate Street; water 4 feet deep in houses in Stockbridge. Sandhill and Quayside flooded.

1835 June 10 Newcastle. Violent thunderstorm. River Derwent overflowed.

1839 June 18 Newcastle. Storm for 2 hours; 'damage almost incredible'. Leazes, Barras Bridge, lake in Newgate Street. Houses flooded to several feet. Boy carried away by flood along Butcher Bank, rescued at corner of Sandhill.

1842 June 22 Allendale. Thunderstorm 3 hours. Bridges and roads damaged requiring several hundred pounds to repair. Agricultural loss.

1846 Aug. 7 Eggleston. Three bridges on Middleton burn carried away. Bridge at Egglesburn damaged. At Eggleston a number of cottages were almost demolished.

1849 Aug. 8 Newcastle. Thunderstorm. Several people struck by lightning. Newgate Street impassable. 60 cartloads of mud later taken away from Gallowgate.

1852 July 5 Widespread thunderstorms. 10 killed by lightning. Flood carried away nearly a mile of the Spennymoor Branch of the Clarence railway and other lines near Ferryhill. Train derailed near Haydon Bridge[20].

1855 July 23 Newbiggin, Teesdale. Thunderstorm caused flood which carried away Newbiggin Bridge over Tees.

1863 Sep. 1 Allendale. Waterspout at Woolly. Water entered flour mill and house at Bridge End. Corn mill 1 yard deep.

1864 May 16 Stocksfield. Thunderstorm. Bridge and two houses at Stocksfield washed away along with much farm produce.

1865 May 22 Allendale/Whitfield. Allen rose to alarming height. Rail bridge at Lipwood 2 miles W of Haydon Bridge carried away.

1871 Apr. 19 Durham. Heavy volume of water down Western Hill to North Road, this and other streets appearing like immense rivers. River Wear soon rose bank high.

1875 July 11 Haydon Bridge. Lightning damage. Storm more violent at Grindon and Sewing Shields[20].

1877 Aug. 21 Hexham. Following rainfall from 17th, a thunderstorm on morning of 21st caused Cockshaw Burn to flood houses in Holy Island and Gilesgate and flooding of tannery. Also Barnard Castle area.

1890 Aug. 12 Newcastle/Sunderland/Durham. Rainfall 2.20 to 2.70 inches in 10 hours. Considerable flooding from poor drainage.

1892 Oct. 3 Lunedale. Flood moved a stone weighing more than 2 tons.

1893 July 2 Alwinton/Bloodybush Edge. Thunderstorm. Bucket survey rainfall of 15 inches at Low Bleakhope. Peat slides covering an area of 30 to 40 acres to Breamish, Usway burn and Alwin. Breamish (Ainsey Burn) rose 40 feet in 30 minutes. Two bridges at Ingram carried away.

1895 June 26 Rothley Lake. Rainfall observation of 3.25 inches in 3.5 hours: observer's house flooded.

1898 Sep. 7 Angerton. Rainfall of 6.70 inches in 3 hours. Two other sites had greater than 4 inches. Damage to roads, excavated to 4 to 5 feet. 18 footbridges washed out.

1900 Oct. 6 Allendale. Both Allens visited by the greatest flood since 1771. Footbridges swept away at Tedham Green, Studdon and Middlehope on the East Allen and at Greenley Cleugh on the West Allen. Swinhope stone bridge undermined and afterwards fell in.

1900 Oct. 20 Morpeth. Tanners Burn. Serious flooding. Rainfall 3.20 to 3.70 inches in 16 hours. Also How Burn.

1907 June 9 Otterburn. Thunderstorm. Houses and Murray Arms flooded to 4 to 5 feet. Two flood plaques. Bridge broken down.

1911 May 14 Bellingham. Thunderstorm on Hareshaw Burn caused serious flooding. 2000 damage. Burn rose 15 feet. Storm lasted 2 hours. Almost every building abutting the banks was wrecked. Two footbridges washed away. Rede and Tyne above Bellingham nearly normal. Hareshaw Drift colliery flooded.

1912 June ? Devil's Water. Thunderstorm. Ham Burn and Rowley burn became raging torrents, the former carrying away all foot bridges.

1927 July 21 Rothbury. Heavy rain for 4 hours. In lower parts of Rothbury water in houses to 4 or 5 feet. Overtopped Tumbleton Lake – engraved flood mark. Flooding also at Reedsmouth and Hexham.

1928 Aug. 29 Newcastle. Flooding in Scotswood and Westmorland Road. Ball lightning in Grainger Market.

1929 Aug. 7 Bellingham. Serious flooding in hilly areas north of Bellingham. North Tyne overflowed banks between Falstone and Chollerford. Crops damaged and lambs drowned.

1930 July 29 Alnwick. 3 hours rainfall. Shambles and Purvis corner flooded and also basement of Midland Bank. Corbridge had rainfall of 1.61 inches in 45 minutes – greenhouse glass broken.

1941 June 22 Newcastle. A succession of severe thunderstorms. Most damage done at Denton Burn. Rainfall 3.74 inches in 85 minutes at highest.

1946 Aug. 13 Rothbury/Edlingham. Thunderstorm followed a period of steady rain. Parts of Rothbury main street under 4 feet of water – into Martins Bank, Queen's Head Hotel and many houses. Sand and stone piled 3 feet high. Electricity failed. Debden and Tumbleton lake dams overtopped and serious damage at the latter – engraved mark. At Edlingham, cottage flooded.

1953 Nov. 12 Alston. Fair Hill dam above Alston overflowed. Flooded scores of houses, some to 5 feet depth. Said to be the third and worst flood in Alston in 2 years. Dam outlets blocked by debris. Continuous rain for 17 hours.

1954 Apr. 3 Fourstones. Two men drowned when struck by a wall of water in South Tyne. Rose 5 to 6 feet in 1/2 hour. They were marooned on a gravel island.

1968 Sep. 13 Morpeth. Intense storm affecting Tanner's burn. Walls around St James Church and graveyard breached. Affected Newgate St, Stanley Tce, Wellway, Copper Close and Staithes Lane. Some houses in Staithes Lane flooded to 2 feet.

1976 June 1 Durham. Flooding of houses in Ushaw Moor, New Brancepeth, East Winning, Brandon and Lanchester after thunderstorm lasting 2 hours.

1981 Aug. 7 Durham/Morpeth. Hail as big as golf balls. Flooding in New Elvet area of Durham.

1983 July 17 Ireshopeburn. Peat slides and flash floods on Ireshope burn, West Grain Langdon beck and West Allen.

1983 July 23 Killhope. Flash flood on Killhope burn.

1986 Aug. 26 Widespread. Hurricane Charley gave highest rainfall over Greta and Tees. Strong winds and rain for 14 hours.

1990 Aug. 24 Isolated cells in North Yorkshire, mid-Durham and north Northumberland with rainfall totals of 87mm at Brignall, 78mm at Smiddy Shaw reservoir and 80mm at Newton Seahouses[21].

REFERENCES
1. Delderfield, E. R. *The Lynmouth Flood Disaster*, (Exmouth, 1953)
2. Dobbie, C. H. and Wolf, P. O. 'The Lynmouth flood of August 1952', *Proc. Instn Civil Engrs* pt 3, (1953)
3. Shaw, E. M. *Hydrology in Practice*, (London, 1988)
4. Bleasdale, A. 'The distribution of exceptionally heavy falls of rain in the United Kingdom 1863-1960', *Jour. Inst. Water Engrs*, 17 (1963)
5. Jackson, M. C. 'Largest two-hour falls of rain in the British Isles', *Weather*, 29 (1974)
6. Anon 'The great rainstorm at Angerton Northumberland September 7th 1898', *British Rainfall 1898*, (1899)
7. Carling, P. A. 'The Noon Hill flash floods; July 17th 1983. Hydrological and geomorphological aspects of a major formative event in an upland landscape', *Trans. Inst. of British Geographers, New Series* 11 (1986)
8. Carling, P. A. 'Peat slides in Teesdale and Weardale, northern Pennines July 1983: description and failure mechanisms', *Earth Surface Processes and Landforms*, 11 (1986)
9. McCahon, C. P., Carling, P. A. and Pascoe, D. 'Chemical and ecological effects of a Pennine peat slide', *Environmental Pollution*, 45 (1987)
10. Acreman, M. C. and Lowing, M. J. 'Maximum flood estimation in the United

Kingdom', *Second National Hydrology Symposium, British Hydrological Society*, Sheffield (1989)

11. Hodgson, J. C. (ed.) *op. cit.* Extracts from the Diary of Christopher Sanderson
12. Camden, W. *Britannia: or a chorographical description of Gt Britain and Ireland together with adjacent islands – revised, digested and large additions made by E Gibson* (London, 1722), p 938
13. Crisp, D. T., Rawes, M. and Welsh, D. 'A Pennine peat slide', *Geographical Journal* 30 (1964)
14. Dixon, D. D. *Upper Coquetdale Northumberland – its History, Traditions, Folklore and Scenery* (1903, reprinted Newcastle upon Tyne, 1973)
15. Latimer, J. *Local Records.*
16. Butler, J. *Memoir of John Grey of Dilston*, (London, 2nd ed. 1874)
17. Rodda, J. C. 'A country-wide study of intense rainfall for the United Kingdom', *Jour. Hydrology* 5 (1967)
18. Rodda, J. C. 'The study of magnitude, frequency and distribution of intense rainfall in the United Kingdom', *British Rainfall 1966*, 3 (1973)
19. Dickenson, G. *Allendale and Whitfield, Historical Notices of the two Parishes*, (Newcastle upon Tyne, 1903)
20. Lees, W. *Historical notes of Haydon Bridge and District*, (Hexham, 1876)
21. Archer, D. R. and Wheeler, D. 'Heavy rainfall in northeast England in August 1990 and some implications for calibration of rainfall radar', *Proc. of the Third National Symposium, British Hydrological Society, Southampton* (1991)

Fig 10.1 'Two Thousand People were in Full Flight', from James Thurber, ' The Day the Dam Broke'.

10. A HISTORY OF FAILURE

And the rain descended, and the floods came, and the wind
blew; and it fell: and great was the fall of it.
Gospel According to St Matthew 7,27

James Thurber tells the tale, in his incomparable style, of the day in Columbus, Ohio, when the dam broke[1] (or to be exact when everybody in town thought that the dam had broken). Amid the cries of 'the dam has broke' and 'Go east, go east', hundreds of people streamed out of town in wild panic, housewives, children, cripples, servants, dogs and cats, the staid and the dignified, firemen, policemen and army officers (Fig 10.1). For two hours the evacuation continued and the fitter or more fearful reached as far as twelve miles out of town. The panic died down only when the runners were eventually reassured that the dam had not broken at all and people returned home sheepishly, minimising their participation in the retreat. Indeed, it became clear that, even if the dam had broken, the part of town where all the running occurred would have been well above the flood waters and had not been in any danger.

Whether Thurber's story is pure fact, pure fiction or some indeterminate mixture of the two, it illustrates the very real fears that may be engendered by the existence of thousands or millions of tons of water dammed back by a bank of earth or a wall of concrete and perched high above villages and farms. In Columbus, Ohio, the fears turned out to be completely unfounded but we may well ask to what extent such fears are ever justified.

Dam failures and their disastrous consequences in other countries reach the headlines periodically. But, in Britain, probably fewer than five hundred people have been killed by dam disasters. Half of these were killed in a single incident when the 29m high dam at Dale Dyke in South Yorkshire failed, in 1864, destroying nearly 800 houses, damaging 4000 others and killing 245 people[2]. Yorkshire was also the scene of the second worst disaster when 81 perished at Holmfirth in 1852[3]. However, compared with, say, the annual toll of death on the roads of over five thousand, the risk of death from dam failure is clearly comparatively modest. The difficulty, however, of making such a comparison is that whereas road death strikes indiscriminately at the whole population, the danger from a dam disaster is directed at a small number of individuals and communities who are subject to a much higher degree of risk. In these circumstances it is appropriate to expect a much higher level of protection.

There has been no loss of life due to dam failure in Britain since 1925. But in that year there were two failures. One incident was at Skelmorie in Scotland in which four people were killed[4] and the other in North Wales in which sixteen people were drowned[2,5]. The latter was a cascade failure, in which the concrete

Eigiau dam had a blow-out and the resulting flood wave exceeded the spillway capacity of the earth embankment at Coedty further downstream. It, in turn, failed and sent an even larger flood down the valley, wreaking havoc in the village of Dolgarrog, and carrying away houses, a church, a school and part of a hotel. The death toll would have been far greater but for the fact that most of the villagers were gathered in the assembly hall just above the level of the flood.

It was these incidents which prompted engineers and politicians to look more closely at dam safety and, in 1930, the Reservoirs (Safety Provisions) Act was passed. This stipulated that all reservoirs with a capacity greater than five million gallons should be regularly inspected by specially qualified engineers. In practice, however, although most large reservoirs owned by water undertakings and other public bodies underwent inspection, many privately-owned dams, including some of considerable size, slipped through the net. Many of these were built before the theories of modern soil mechanics and hydrology were fully appreciated. Indeed, some were built with scant attention to the best available theory and practice of their own day. Failures continued to occur but fortunately, and perhaps fortuitously, without loss of life. As a consequence it was felt necessary to strengthen the Act to ensure that these dams also received full inspection and supervision. Thus the Reservoirs Act was passed in 1975 and, in spite of continued opposition from some authorities who felt that implementation could result in large and unnecessary costs of remedial work, it was finally put on the Statute Book in 1986.

But what of Northumbria? Surely there have been no dam failures here? In fact, my research has revealed no less than eleven dam failures and several further instances of dam overtopping when failure could easily have occurred. Most of these dams and reservoirs were of sufficient size to come within the ambit of the Reservoirs Act. Their locations are shown in Fig 10.2 and you can see that they are fairly evenly distributed over the Northumbrian area. The earliest failure occurred around 1700 and the most recent in 1987. I will describe these in chronological order.

1. Shildon Lough near Corbridge –*c*.1700 NGR 45.025665

Mackenzie[6] reports an incident around 1700 when a great quantity of rain fell on Shildon Lough near Corbridge at the commencement of harvest when the lough overflowed and burst like a deluge to the westward, sweeping away crops and fences. 'At Corbridge East Field the water turned into the Tyne leaving immense numbers of pike in every standing pool; nor did the Lough ever after contain so many fish. A pleasure boat used to be kept on it and wild ducks resorted thereto.' In the mid-eighteenth century, Shildon common was drained and converted to pasture and, although the site of the reservoir can be located, there are no remaining signs of the dam.

2. Otterburn – 15th September 1839 NGR 35.883932
There was widespread flooding in the north-east in mid-September 1839, but

particularly along the Wansbeck and North Tyne and their tributaries[7]. The village of Otterburn, no stranger to flooding, was severely affected. The rising waters of the burn overtopped the banks and spread through the village along the double row of houses. At 4 a.m. on 15 September, the houses nearest to the stream were already half full. But, at 4.30 a.m., the level increased another two feet in five minutes and the water spread more extensively into all except two of the houses. The ground floors of those near the river were said to be nearly full of water. There was a danger of the bridge being swept away but, at 4.45 a.m., a wall gave way and the river created a new channel. The cause of this abrupt rise was the failure of dams impounding two fish ponds, the larger of considerable depth and occupying 2.7 ha (6 acres). The remains of this dam can still be seen two hundred metres upstream from the A686 road bridge. There are remnants of a control gate opening which presumably formed part of the spillway. Upstream stone protection and access steps for fishing are still visible.

3. Netherwitton – 15th September 1839 NGR 45.100900

The village of Netherwitton is situated on the banks of the river Font, a tributary of the Wansbeck which, in the storm that caused the failure at Otterburn, was at its highest level for several decades. Latimer[8] notes that a dam at Netherwitton was destroyed. The site of this dam has not yet been identified.

4. Kildale – 22nd July 1840 NGR 45.604097 and 45.627098

A dam impounding a fish pond existed at Kildale on the river Leven since the Middle Ages. It was located just behind the fortified manor house of the Percy family and probably provided fish on Fridays for the baronial household. Another larger earth embankment was built two kilometres upstream in about 1831, probably by the Bell-Livesey family who then held the Kildale estate. The remains of the upper dam can still be clearly seen, cut through by the railway from Teesside to Whitby.

In the early morning of 22 July, there was an intense rainstorm centred on Commondale in the headwaters of the Leven. The Rev. J. Ibbetson, Vicar at Ayton, records what happened, in the parish register[9].

It filled the upper lake at Kildale, near Westhouse, so that the weir of it, tho' 3 feet deep and 40 feet wide could not contain the water issuing – it therefore ran over all the length of the embankment. During the previous 9 years since the formation of the lake, the water was never known to be above 10 inches deep on the weir. About 3 o'clock a.m., the embankment gave way and the water rushed over the adjacent fields with great fury carrying down the two stone bridges between the upper and lower lakes. The lower lake endured the augmented torrent for another hour or more until the great part of the upper lake had passed into it, then it burst and came down the narrow defile with great fury and rapidity. An old mill, about the eighth-of-a-mile below Kildale church was completely swept away, the very foundations could not be traced in the washen rock, a Bleaching Mill a quarter-of-a-mile lower was nearly all washed down and many trees etc. washed up and thrown together in the wildest confusion!

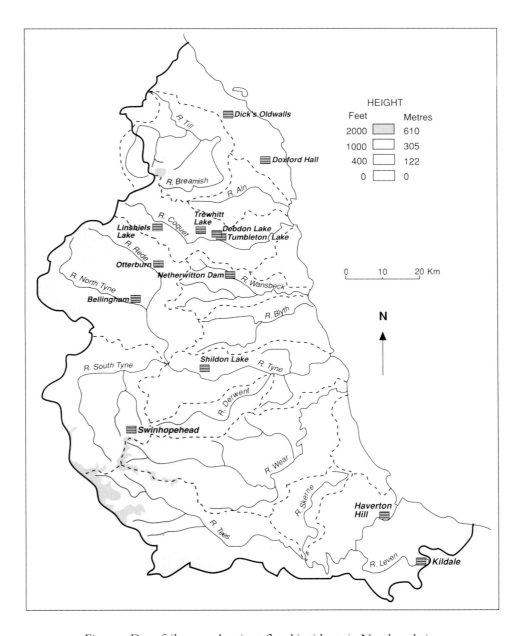

Fig 10.2 Dam failures and serious flood incidents in Northumbria.

The destruction in towns and villages downstream is described in Chapter 4. The failure was followed by a court case in which downstream residents sued the dam owner. Details of the case have not been found, but the local tradition is that the dam owner escaped prosecution as the event was claimed to be an Act of God.

The description of the weir provides a basis for assessing the severity of the event. Assuming a standard weir shape, the flow with the weir covered to a depth of three feet would be about 15 m³/sec but, as the depth exceeded the height of the weir and flowed over the whole dam, the flow was probably much greater. Modern methods of calculation based on the National Environment Research Council, *Flood Studies Report*[10], show that such a flood on its catchment area of 3.3 square kilometres could be expected to recur on average only once in five thousand years. Perhaps there was some justification in considering it an Act of God.

5. Haverton Hill – 5th September 1931 NGR 45.493233

In spite of the unusual frequency and severity of flooding during the latter half of the nineteenth century, it was another hundred years before the next reported dam failure occurred. It followed very heavy rainfall over south–east Durham and North Yorkshire on 4 September 1931. The *North-Eastern Daily Gazette* reported the event as follows:

The new flood disaster at Haverton Hill is the direct consequence of the overflowing of Greatham Creek and the bursting of a small works reservoir. The creek rose with alarming rapidity and overflowed to the low lying area known as Haverton Hill Marshes. The water spread from here and washed away part of the side of a reservoir belonging to the Salt Union. This interfered with the ability of the reservoir to carry its exceptionally heavy load and the side gave way. Water rushed down into a large sunken area and flooded this to a depth of about 10 feet. Here on account of previous flooding, a substantial wall had been constructed but the weight of water caused this to break and water rushed unimpeded through part of the Salt Union Works into Ash Street and Oak Street. In the former, eight houses were flooded and in the latter, three houses were evacuated. One woman returned home to find that the water was waist deep in her kitchen and sitting room.

This extraordinary flooding happened at a time when the rain-storm had ceased and people were congratulating themselves on being immune from the effects of the heavy rainfall. It happened without any warning and it was some time before the people could understand the source of such a large volume of water in the neighbourhood.

The reservoir, which was used for industrial purposes, was subsequently rebuilt and strengthened and still exists. The area of housing downstream has been demolished.

6. Tumbleton Lake – 13th August 1946 NGR 46.070025

The next series of reservoir incidents occurred in the late 1940s during two of the Border floods (Chapter 8). In the first of these, torrential rain swept across Northumberland on Monday night 12 August 1946, culminating in a thunderstorm over Rothbury in the early hours of Tuesday morning. Two dams, Debden Lake and Tumbleton Lake on the nearby Cragside estate (now a National Trust property), were overtopped and Tumbleton lake came close to failure[11]. The overflow channel was destroyed and a bridge over it was carried away. The flood water which rose over the earth embankment caused scouring on the downstream face of the dam. Although this is often a precursor to failure by breaching, in this instance the dam survived. However, the structure was so impaired that the reservoir was kept empty for many years afterwards. The flood level is recorded on an engraved flood mark on a boathouse adjacent to the spillway. Here also is recorded the level of a previous flood which overtopped the dam to a lesser extent on 21 July 1927.

7. Dick's Oldwalls – 12th August 1948 NGR 46.074345

Just two years later, there was an even more widespread and intense rainfall over the Border country, with rainfalls over 150mm being recorded in the Tweed Valley. The storm extended as far north as Edinburgh and there are reports by Baxter[12] of a cascade failure of two dams in the Dunbar area. However, one dam failure in North Northumberland, near Belford, appears to have escaped the notice of the press at the time. An earth embankment with the rather remarkable name of Dick's Oldwalls, situated on a small unnamed tributary of Ross Low, was overtopped and failed. The resulting downstream flood wave, combined with the already high flow, struck a lower reservoir at Middleton Hall. It too was overtopped but, remarkably, survived, although property downstream was flooded to a depth of half a metre. Dick's Oldwalls appears to have been built to high engineering standards between the wars. It had a concrete spillway which was simply inadequate for the large flood discharge.

Until recently the breached dam was concealed beneath a dense woodland cover. Trees were felled on the downstream side in 1992 and the triangular breach is now clearly visible (Plate 10.1).

On the same occasion, it is reported that a small dam at Doxford Hall, fifteen kilometres to the south-east, was also overtopped. Mr Lionel Mark who still resides at the site, tells how he walked across the dam with the water flowing over the top to the depth of his wellingtons – a brave but foolhardy escapade.

8. Trewhitt Lake – 6th March 1963 NGR 36.992047

All the previously reported failures occurred as the result of intense rainstorms during the summer months. This is the only failure that can definitely be ascribed to melting snow and ice. It is also the only reservoir for which we have an eyewitness account of the actual failure. After the prolonged freeze-up in the first two months of 1963, reservoirs and even rivers had a solid cover of ice of more than 0.3 metres in thickness. Drifted snow in some parts of the upper Coquet valley lay level with the tops of telegraph poles. The ensuing thaw commenced on 5 March; temperatures rose rapidly and the melting snow delivered nearly two months of accumulated precipitation to the rivers in a couple of days. Press attention was concentrated on events in Morpeth (Chapter 7) on the lower Wansbeck, but the Coquet and all its tributaries also reached

Plate 10.1 Dick's Oldwalls dam, near Belford, Northumberland. Failed 13 August 1948.
Photo. D. Archer.

exceptionally high levels. With the rising flow, Trewhitt lake, a reservoir on Foxton burn, began to fill. The cover of ice lifted, cracked and broke into large ice floes. Some of these became wedged in the vertical shaft spillway (Plate 10.2) and reduced its capacity to carry the floodwaters just at the time when that capacity was most needed. The water level gradually crept up to the lowest point on the dam crest and began spilling over on the downstream face. Erosion of the crest commenced shortly and a resident at Low Trewhitt recollects that the triangular breach grew rapidly to the full 5 metres depth of the dam in less than twenty minutes (Plate 10.3). Fortunately for the village of Thropton downstream, the intervening valley is comparatively flat, so that flood waters were able to spread out and dissipate and only a few houses in the lower part of the village were flooded.

9. Swinhopehead Dam – Late 1960s NGR 35.828468
Swinhopehead dam is an impressive structure when viewed from the bleak moorland of Shivery Hill where the minor road from Nenthead to Spartylea crosses the head of the Swinhope Valley (a tributary of the East Allen). Even more striking is the gap near the southern end of the dam. Closer inspection reveals the broken remains of a concrete spillway channel downstream of the breach.

Swinhopehead was the largest of the dams built in the late nineteenth century to service the Pennine lead-mining industry. Around the turn of the century,

Plate 10.2 Trewhitt Lake dam, upstream face and drop shaft spillway. *Photo. D. Archer.*

Plate 10.4 Swinhopehead dam, Allendale, Northumberland. Downstream face and remains of concrete overflow spillway channel. *Photo. D. Archer.*

Plate 10.3 Trewhitt Lake dam, near Rothbury, Northumberland. Breach and downstream face. *Photo. D. Archer.*

the industry began to decline and the dam and associated mines changed hands a number of times before eventually being abandoned in the 1950s.

By the early 1960s, local residents report that the condition of the spillway structure was deteriorating and this flaw was probably the cause of its downfall. Erosion around the base of the concrete overflow channel probably provided a pathway for the water through the clay core, progressively enlarging the gap in each flood event (Plate 10.4). The final failure was probably not sudden and catastrophic as there was no flooding of the potentially affected property at Low Swinhope Shield and indeed the occupant did not recall a significant flood. The date and even the year of failure is uncertain, but was most likely between 1964 and 1968.

10. Low Dam Bellingham – 13th September 1968 NGR 35.843837
The Low Dam on the Hareshaw burn on the outskirts of Bellingham provided a source of power for the Hareshaw iron works built by the Duke of Northumberland in 1838[13]. The water offtake from the dam drove a seventy horsepower waterwheel for the blast furnaces. The iron works operated for only ten years; the high cost of delivery to markets on Tyneside without the benefit of railway transport made the plant quite uneconomic. (The Border Counties Railway did not reach Bellingham until 1860.) Although abandoned and probably without maintenance, the dam stood for over a hundred years.

The dam was built at the site of a natural rock bar and waterfall. The dam face was a solid masonry wall, a single block, approximately 0.9 metres in thickness, and standing more than eight metres high (Plate 10.5). It was keyed in to two massive lateral buttresses but the horizontal courses of blocks were not keyed together and the dam depended for its stability largely on the weight of the stonework. During low to moderate flows, water spilled through two rectangular slots below the crest, but the slots were filled occasionally in flood and the water spilled over the full crest width.

On the day of the great Bellingham flood of 14 May 1911, when houses were torn apart just a few hundred metres downstream (Chapter 9), the water not only filled the crest but also spread out over adjoining fields and cut behind the buttresses. On that occasion the dam survived but it failed in another test of its strength on 13 September 1968.

That unlucky Friday evening was marked by isolated intense rain storms over many parts of Northumberland, including Morpeth. Tommy Brechons of Foundry Farm near the dam recalls the intense thunder and lightning which seemed centred between Bellingham and West Woodburn, and his difficulty in returning home through flooded roads. At the dam, the spillway slots were blocked with debris, and it is probable that tree trunks torn from the wooded dene pounded against the dam face. Sometime during the late evening, the structure slipped forward on its basal course of masonry, bulging in the middle and tearing the keystones in the buttresses before collapsing like a heap of cards. Surprisingly, the channel downstream, which had been enlarged after the flood

Plate 10.5 Low dam, Bellingham, Northumberland during the flood of 14 May 1911. Note the massive buttresses and the water by-passing at both ends.

of 1907, held most of the flow and there was no repeat of the earlier disaster. But Arthur Baty, whose home at Parkside Place adjoins the river at the bridge, could hear the roar of the water and the large masonry blocks being rolled along. Next morning the blocks lay in a heap where they had come to rest against the wooden bridge, just upstream from the Tyne confluence where the velocity of the water had been checked.

11. Linshiels Lake – 1987 NGR 36.892043

Linshiels Lake is situated on a headwater tributary of the river Coquet and, because of its location within the restricted zone of the Otterburn ranges, it is not frequently seen by the general public. There was a natural lake but its storage volume was trebled by the construction of an earth embankment. The first inspection under the Reservoirs Act was planned in April 1987 but it was called off when it was discovered that the dam had already failed and the lake had returned to its natural size. The exact date of failure is unknown but rainfall records from nearby Linbriggs show no extreme amounts of rain or snowmelt over the preceding winter and spring. A clue to the cause may lie in the rumours amongst residents in the upper Coquet that, during the previous autumn, two craters had been observed near the crest of the structure. It may well be that gunners on the range or from the air had been attempting to emulate the exploits of their illustrious military forebears. Such craters could certainly have created a weakness which was vulnerable even to moderate rainfall. The final episode in this catalogue of failure appears therefore, to have been more a consequence of 'fire' than of flood.

PROSPECTS FOR THE FUTURE

This historic sequence of incidents appears to give some justification to concern about dam safety. The tally of eleven failures, albeit over three centuries, is a significant proportion of the number of dams in existence and registered under the Reservoirs Act with the county councils.

However, following the implementation of the Reservoirs Act 1975, the situation has radically changed. *All* dams impounding in excess of 25,000 cubic metres must now undergo a major inspection every ten years and any deficiencies in the structure or the overflow channel must be put right. Each dam must also have a supervising engineer who maintains more regular surveillance. Many private dams have recently being inspected for the first time and work is being carried out to improve their flood capacities and structural stability[14]

Although the possibility of failure in some future extraordinary flood cannot be eliminated entirely, the work now being done will reduce the risk to a minute level.

REFERENCES

1. Thurber, J. 'The Day the Dam Broke', from *My Life and Hard Times*, (Hamish Hamilton, London, 1963)
2. Smith, N. *History of Dams*, (London, 1971)
3. Hughes, A. 'The erosion resistance of compacted clay fills when subject to overtopping', PhD Thesis, University of Newcastle upon Tyne, 1981
4. Anon. 'Bursting of Skelmorie reservoir', *Water and Water Engineering*, 27 (1925)
5. Anon. 'The dam disaster in North Wales', *The Engineer*, 140 (1925)
6. MacKenzie, E. *View of the County of Northumberland and of those parts of the County of Durham situated north of the River Tyne, with Berwick upon Tweed and Brief Noices of Celebrated Places, on the Scottish Border*, (2 vols, Newcastle upon Tyne, 1825)
7. Richardson, M. A. *Memorials of Floods*
8. Latimer, J. *Local Records of Remarkable events*
9. Blakeborough, J. F. *Bits of West Cleveland; Great Ayton, Stokesley and District, Past and Present*, (Middlesborough 1901), includes quotations from Revd. J. Ibbetson in Ayton Baptism Register 1835-79.
10. Natural Environment Research Council, *Flood Studies Report*, (London, 1975)
11. Anon. Report on the Debden and Tumbleton Lakes at Cragside, for Lord Armstrong's Trustees, (1946)
12. Baxter, G. 'Rainfall and flooding on South-east Scotland 12 August 1948', *Jour. Inst. of Water Engrs*, 3 (1949)
13. Charlton, B. *Upper North Tynedale – a Northumbrian Valley and its people*, (Northumbrian Water, 1987)
14. Institution of Civil Engineers *Floods and Reservoir Safety – an Engineering Guide*, (London, 1978)

SELECT BIBLIOGRAPHY

Bell, J. *An account of the Great Flood in the River Tyne on Saturday morning December 30 1815, to which is added, A Narrative of the Great Flood in the River Tyne, Tease and Wear etc on 16th and 17th November 1771*, (Newcastle upon Tyne, 1816)

British Rainfall published annually as *Symon's British Rainfall*, 1860 to 1900 and as *British Rainfall*, (HMSO, 1900 to 1968)

Brooks, C. E. P. and Glasspoole, J. *British Floods and Droughts*, (London, 1928)

Duncan, W. Local newspaper cuttings 1878-1915. Unpublished annual compilation, Newcastle upon Tyne Public Library

Fordyce, T. *Local Records or Historical Register of Remarkable Events which have occurred in Northumberland and Durham*, (2 vols, Newcastle upon Tyne, 1867 and 1876)

Garret, W. *An Account of the Great Floods in the Rivers Tyne, Tees, Wear, Eden etc in 1771 and 1815* [by W Garrett] who acknowledged the loan of John Adamson's collection of original documents relative to the flood of 1771, Topographical Society's Publication, Miscellaneous IV, 5

Jones, P. D., Ogilvie A. E. and Wigley, T. M. L. 'Riverflow Data for the United Kingdom: Reconstructed Data back to 1844 and Historical Data back to 1556', *University of East Anglia, Climatic Research Unit, Research Report 8*, (1984)

Lamb. H. H. Climate: *Present, Past and Future*, (London, 1977)

Latimer, J. *Local Records or Historical Register of Remarkable Events which have occurred in Northumberland and Durham, Newcastle upon Tyne and Berwick upon Tweed, being a continuation of the work under the same title published by the late Mr Sykes*, (Newcastle upon Tyne, 1857)

Potter, H. R. 'The use of historic records for the augmentation of hydrological data', *Institute of Hydrology Report 46* (1978)

Richardson, M. A. *The Borderer's Table Book or Gathering of the Local History and Romance of the English and Scottish Border*, Historical Division (5 vols, Newcastle upon Tyne, 1846)

Richardson, M. A. *Memorials of the Floods in the Rivers of Northumberland and Durham*, (Newcastle upon Tyne, 1849)

Sykes, J. *Local records or Historical Register of Remarkable Events from the Earliest Period of Authentic Record to the Present Time*, (Newcastle upon Tyne, 1833)

NEWSPAPERS CONSULTED
(with dates of publication to the present unless otherwise noted)

Berwick Advertiser	1808–
Berwick Journal and N. Northumberland News	1855–
Alnwick Mercury	1854–1883
Northumberland Gazette	
(Alnwick and County Gazette)	1883–
Morpeth Herald	1854–
Hexham Courant	1864–
Hexham Herald	1868–1926
Newcastle Courant	1711–1910
The Journal (Newcastle Journal)	1739–1788 and 1832–
Newcastle Weekly Chronicle	1764–1953
Evening Chronicle	1885–
Auckland Times and Herald	
(Bishop Auckland Herald)	1854–1910
Auckland Chronicle	1866–
Durham Advertiser	1814–
Durham Chronicle	1820–
Sunderland Herald	1831–1906
Sunderland Times (Northern Times)	1839–1914
Sunderland Daily Echo	1873–
Northern Echo	1870–
Teesdale Mercury	1855–
Darlington and Stockton Times	1848–
Darlington Telegraph	1854–1858
Northeastern Daily Gazette	
York Courant	1728–1848
Yorkshire Gazette	1819–1954

A list of all newspapers published in Northumberland and Durham with dates of publication and location of copies is provided in:

Manders, F. W. D. *Northumberland and Durham, Bibliography of British Newspapers*, (1982)

INDEX

Figures in **bold** refer to illustrations

abstraction, 17, 131: control of, 154
Acomb: flood stone, 108 afforestation, See Floods, forest influence on
Ainsey burn, 194
Aldin Grange, 75, 78
Alemouth Turnpike, 100
Allen, river, 89
Allendale, 93, **101**, 192-4
Allenheads, 115
Allensford, 92, 111
Allerwash burn, 187
Allery burn, 131, 142-3
alluvial rivers, 17, 41, 153, 173
Aln, river, 5, **148**, 149, 154-5, 158-9, 161-3, 171, 173
Alnham, **148**, 149
Alnmouth, 100, **148**, 149, 163
Alnwick, **148**, 155-6, 160-2, 164, 168, 186-7, 190, 194
Alston, 88, **90**, 93, 105, 110, 112, 120, 194
Alwin, river, 149, **150**, 186, 194
Alwinton, 149, **150**, 153, 186, 194
Amble, 149, **150**
andesite, 151
Angerton, 178-81, **180**, 194
Annie Island, 114
area: units of, 12
armouring layer, 102, 174
Ash gill, **86**, 89
Ashington, **130**
Axwell Park, 111
Aycliffe, 43, 45

Balder, river, **16**, 28, 185

Balderhead reservoir, **16**, 31
Balderdale, 25, 185, 192
Bangladesh, floods in, 9
Bar Gap, 34
Bardon Mill, 89, 123
Barforth, 23
Barnard Castle, **16**, 17, 19, 22-3, 26-28, 32, 193
barrage, Tees, 37
Baydale beck, **42**, 47
Beal, 167
Beamish, 115
Beaufront, 119
Beaumont, T. W., 111
Bedburn beck, **66**, 68
Belford, **148**, 156, 159-60, 167, 202
Belford burn, 159
Bellasis bridge, 147
Bellingham, 89, **90**, 104, 112, 119-20, 123, 186-7, **188-9**, 192, 194, **200**: Low dam at, 187, 205-6, **206**
Bellister, 93-4
Bense bridge, 60
Benwell, 112
Berwick-upon-Tweed, **148**, 154-5
Bewick mill, 149, 153
Bill Point, 112
Billingham, **16**
Bilton, 159
Binchester, 82
Birtley, 117
Bishop Auckland, **66**, 68, 75, 77, 79
Bizzle, The, 151
Blackett, Sir Walter, 100, 102

Blackton reservoir, 31
Blackwell, 23, 25, 29, 32
Blanchland, 89, 111
Blankenbergs' collection, 187
Blaydon, 89, **90**, 109, 111-4
Bleakhope, 149
Bloodybush Edge, **150**, 186, 194
Blyth, **130**
Blyth, river, 2, 5, 7, 129, **130**, 146-7
Board of Health, 74-5, 136
Bolam, 179, 181
Bollihope burn, **66**, 68
Border: and catchment boundaries, 89, 153-4
Border Counties Railway, 104, 112, 116, 205
Border floods, 1, 163-8, 201
Bothal, 129, 134, 136-8
Boulby, 50, 52
boulder clay, 41
Bowes, 39, 193
Bowmont Water, **148**, 149, 151, 153-4, 156, 158, 161, 165
Bracken Hill, 71, 192
Bradbury, 41, **42**, 46-8
Brafferton, **42**, 49
braided rivers, 89, 174
Bramwell, Rev, 21-2, 24
Brandon, **148**, 153, 160-1, 165
Branton, 158
Breamish, river, 2, **148**, 149, 151, 153, 158, 160-1, 165, 167-8, 171, 186, 194
bridges: failure of, at Allendale, 93; at

211